D1431175

LIVING BIOGRAPHIES OF
Great Scientists

Great Scientists

Euclid

Schnittkind, Henry Thomas.

LIVING BIOGRAPHIES OF

Great Scientists

By HENRY THOMAS, *pseud.* AND

DANA LEE THOMAS, *pseud.*

Illustrations by
GORDON ROSS

PROPERTY OF
CARNEGIE INSTITUTE OF TECHNOLOGY
LIBRARY

Nelson Doubleday, Inc.
GARDEN CITY, NEW YORK

925
S 36 L

COPYRIGHT, 1941
BY GARDEN CITY PUBLISHING CO., INC.

CL
PRINTED IN THE UNITED STATES OF AMERICA

Contents

[*v*]

CONTENTS

Introduction

THE READER OF BIOGRAPHY lives not one life but many lives. For he expands his own experiences by adding to them the experiences of his fellow men. He sees the world, so to speak, through many pairs of eyes and he thus learns to contact his neighbors through many sympathetic chords of understanding.

Every biography is a window which enables us to look into a different angle of reality. This is especially true of the biographies of the great scientists. For the scientists have made it their business to decipher the secret of reality and to translate it into the practical language of our everyday life.

The scientists—the thinkers and the doers of our human family —have brought down to the rest of us a twofold blessing from the "thousand several watchtowers" of their superior wisdom. They have showed us our unimportance, and they have enabled us to become more important. They have defined our place in nature—an insignificant ant-heap of humanity infesting a tiny mudball of pebbles and dust hidden away in one of the obscurest corners of the universe. A sobering and yet at the same time an ennobling thought. Each of us is but a mean atom of the universe, yet each of us is an atom of no mean universe. And thanks to the efforts of the scientists each of us is able, through the practical application of the laws of astronomy, physics, chemistry, mathematics, medicine and biology, to develop into a happier, healthier and more efficient citizen of the universe.

And a wiser citizen? Unfortunately, not yet. The scientists give us our instruments for healing, and we turn them into weapons for killing. But this is the fault of the pupils and not of the teachers. The human heart seems to be a less apt scholar than the human mind. The moral development of the human race has lagged far behind its mental development. But here, too, the lives of the scientists can serve as our guide. Most of them have demonstrated by their own actions that the greater the knowledge, the greater the humility. Every significant advance in science, as nearly every great scientist has acknowledged, is the result of the combined thought of many minds. A true understanding of the world—and this seems to be the practically universal verdict of the scientists—points to reciprocal coöperation as the surest roadway to individual happiness.

H. T.
D. L. T.

ARCHIMEDES

Great Scientific Contributions by Archimedes

INVENTIONS:

The Screw of Archimedes for making water run "up-hill."

The pulley.

SCIENTIFIC TREATISES:

On the Sphere and Cylinder.

The Measurement of the Circle.

On Conoids and Spheroids.

On Spirals.

The Center of Gravity.

On Floating Bodies.

The Sand Reckoner.

The Method of Mechanics.

Geometrical Propositions.

The Cattle Problem.

Archimedes

Archimedes

287 B.C.–212 B.C.

Hiero, the king of Syracuse, had given his jeweler a certain weight of gold to be fashioned into a crown. When the crown was finished, the suspicion arose in Hiero's mind that his jeweler had stolen part of the gold and replaced it with an equal quantity of silver. Accordingly he commissioned his court scientist, Archimedes, to detect the fraud if possible.

After many days of fruitless research, Archimedes was about to abandon the task. But one morning, as he stepped into his tub at the public bathhouse of Syracuse, he noticed the overflow of the water. The sight of this overflow set his imagination aflame. Forgetting his naked condition, he leaped out of his bathtub and ran home through the streets of Syracuse crying, *"Eureka! Eureka!—I have found it! I have found it!"*

What he had found was a simple solution to his problem about Hiero's crown. He would procure two masses of metal, one of gold and one of silver, and each of equal weight with the crown. Then he would in turn submerge each of the three masses—the gold, the silver and the crown—in a vessel filled with water and measure the overflow of the water in each of the three cases.

As soon as possible he put this idea to the test and discovered that the amount of water displaced by the crown was more than the amount of water displaced by the gold, and less than the amount of water displaced by the silver. And in this way he knew that the crown consisted neither entirely of gold nor entirely of silver, but that it was a mixture of both.

This simple method of comparing the weights of solids with the weights of equal quantities of water supplied Hiero with the solution to the mystery of the crown. But it supplied the rest of mankind with a far greater gift—the key to the solution of one of the profound mysteries of nature, the so-called "specific gravity" of the various substances which go into the making of the world. This law of specific gravity, known to the present day as the *Principle of Archimedes,* may be briefly stated as follows: "A body immersed in a fluid loses as much in weight as the weight of an equal volume of the fluid."

Thus it was in the simple process of bathing that Archimedes discovered one of the great secrets of nature. Yet bathing to Archimedes, it is interesting to note, was not an ordinary process. Rather it was an extraordinary event. So absorbed was he in his scientific experiments that, to quote Plutarch, "his servants with the greatest difficulty, and against his will, got him to the baths to wash and anoint him." And when finally they succeeded in luring him to the baths, continues Plutarch, "he would ever draw all sorts of geometrical figures with his fingers upon his naked body."

Geometry was his greatest passion. "Intoxicated and ravished with the sweet enticements of this siren, which as it were lay continually with him, he often forgot his meat and his drink." He lived in the springtime of the mathematical sciences—an era in which the manipulations of numbers and the measurements of triangles and circles were amongst the most exciting of adventures in the academies and the colleges of the Greek world. The magic of Euclid, the "Father of Geometry," still lay like a bloom over an enchanted age. This professor of mathematics at the University of Alexandria had transformed the earth and the heavens into a vast design of intricate configurations. And with the deft fingers of his amazing intellect he had taken this design apart and analyzed it into its simple components—points, lines, angles, curves, surfaces, solids—a map of the infinite translated into the finite language of elementary mathematics. Euclid made the impossible possible by the simplest of methods. When his fellow professors at Alexandria told him that there was no human way to measure the height of the Great Pyramid, he proceeded to measure it as follows: He waited for that hour of the day when the length of his shadow was exactly equal to the height of his person, and then he measured the length of the pyramid's shadow. "This, gentlemen," he said, "is the exact height of the Great Pyramid."

Though he simplified his geometry, Euclid insisted upon a thorough study of its principles in order that his students might fully understand them. The story is told that Ptolemy, the king of Alexandria, once expressed his impatience at Euclid's elaborate manner of explaining his theorems. "Isn't there," asked the king, "a shorter way of learning geometry than through your method?"

"Sire," replied Euclid, "in the country there are two kinds of roads—the hard road for the common people and the easy road for the royal family. But in geometry all must go the same way. There is no royal road to learning."

As to the details of Euclid's life, very little is known about them. One legend has it that the last—and best—section of his famous *Elements of Geometry* was thrown into the fire by his wife in a fit of temper. If this story is true, the probability is that his wife lost her temper through no provocation on Euclid's part. For he was, the ancient writers tell us, "a gentle and kindly old man." His students idolized him. For he "guided them like a father." Yet on occasion he could tame the more impertinent of his "children" with the lash of a biting sarcasm. "Can you tell me," asked one of his students after he had learned the first theorem, "just what practical advantage there is in studying geometry?" Whereupon Euclid turned to his servant. "Grumio,"

[5]

he said, "give this gentleman a dollar; he can't learn without money."

Euclid himself, like most of the ancient Greek scholars, cared little for the "practical" values of his scientific investigations. He loved learning for learning's sake. Shy, modest and aloof, he "lived peaceably in his habitation" and allowed the world of petty politics and of military glory to clatter by in its noisy and vulgar parade. "These things," he said, "shall pass. But the designs of the heavenly stars shall remain eternally fixed."

II

QUITE different from this dispassionate life of quiet contemplation was the career of Archimedes, the "spiritual grandson" of Euclid. (Archimedes was the pupil of Conon, who was the pupil of Euclid.) As a young man he desired, like his great predecessor, to devote himself exclusively to mathematics. He continued the study of geometry from the point where Euclid had left off. He calculated the ratio of the circumference of a circle to its diameter; he devised a plan for counting the sand on the seashore; he formulated a method for measuring the areas and the volumes of circular and of spherical objects; and he discovered the relation between the volume of a cylinder and that of an inscribed ball. This last discovery was as simple as it was ingenious. He constructed a cylindrical cup whose height was equal to its diameter, and a sphere that fitted snugly into this cup. He then filled the cup with water, immersed the sphere in the water, and compared the amount of the overflow with the original amount of the water in the cylinder. He thus found that the volume of an inscribed sphere is equal to exactly two-thirds of the volume of its enclosing cylinder. So proud was he of this discovery that he ordered the figure of a sphere within a cylinder to be carved upon his tombstone.

For Archimedes, like Euclid, was anxious to be remembered

only as a philosophical mathematician. He wanted to be left alone to his geometrical studies. But the insistent demands of his environment compelled him to become an inventor as well as a philosopher. Archimedes thoroughly disliked his compulsory role as "a maker of the vile and beggarly and mercenary machines of commerce and war." But he was related to Hiero and therefore felt constrained by a double obligation—as a subject and as a kinsman—to obey the orders of the king.

Working under these orders, Archimedes produced no less than forty inventions—some of them for commercial use but most of them for military purposes. Perhaps the most interesting of his commercial inventions was the so-called *Screw of Archimedes*. This hollow corkscrew, placed upon an inclined surface with the lower end immersed in a pool of water and with the spirals turning constantly from left to right, scoops up the water at the bottom and spills it out at the top—thus compelling the water to perform the apparently impossible "miracle" of flowing uphill.

This commercial invention—employed even today for the draining of swampy areas in the Netherlands—was to the contemporaries of Archimedes an object of profound amazement. But more amazing than his "utensils of peace" were his engines of war. His native city of Syracuse was besieged by the Romans, and King Hiero called upon Archimedes to devise weapons of defense against this siege. A Roman fleet, under the leadership of Marcellus, had set sail against Syracuse. "I believe I can destroy that fleet," said Archimedes.

"By what means?" asked Hiero.

"By means of burning mirrors."

Hiero said nothing, but shook his head. His poor kinsman had apparently lost his reason through overstudy.

Yet Archimedes made good his boast. For, "as soon as the ships of the enemy came within bowshot of Syracuse," he trained upon them the battery of his mirrors which he had constructed especially for the purpose. These mirrors were "huge concave plates of metal" so designed as to focus the blazing light of the sun upon the oncoming fleet.

In connection with this story it is interesting to note that Sir Isaac Newton, after a series of experiments with concave mirrors, expressed his opinion that such an invention on the part of Archimedes was not beyond the realm of scientific possibility. Most of the historians, however, reject the incident as fictitious, since no account of it is found either in Plutarch or in Polybius, the two leading authorities on the life of Archimedes.

But there seems to be little disagreement among the leading historians as to the authenticity of his other military inventions. When the blockade around Syracuse had become a serious threat to the further existence of the city, Hiero again called his kinsman to his aid. "Is it possible," he asked, "to remove the enemy's ships?"

"Yes," replied Archimedes. "It is possible even to remove the earth."

"Just what do you mean?"

"Merely this—that if I had a place in another world in which to plant my feet, I could wrench the earth out of its course." He then went on to explain his theory of levers and pulleys—a discovery of his own—by means of which he could move a maximum of weight with a minimum of effort.

When Hiero expressed his doubt as to the efficacy of this plan, Archimedes proceeded to put it to the test. He constructed a multiple pulley, attached the chain at one end of the pulley to a large and heavily laden Syracusan ship, and handed the rope at the other end of the pulley to Hiero. "Pull the rope, Sire, and see what happens."

The king pulled the rope, and a cry of astonishment escaped from his lips. For the feeble effort of his two small hands had lifted the ship as if by magic out of the water and dangled it into the air.

It was not long before Marcellus, too, was to marvel at the "magic" of Archimedes. The Roman commander had arrived before the walls of Syracuse equipped with "a fleet of sixty vessels filled with all sorts of arms and missiles." Moreover, he had erected "an engine of artillery on a huge platform supported by eight galleys fastened together." But all this stupendous armada was merely a handful of toys in the enormous iron grappling hooks that were attached to the pulleys of Archimedes. Descending upon the Roman ships like birds of prey, these "iron claws" of Archimedes drew them "straight up into the air, and then plunged them stern foremost into the depths." At times, to vary his defensive strategy, Archimedes carried the enemy's galleys "high over the cliffs that jutted out beneath the walls of the city, and then whirled them around and around and finally dashed them with all their merchandise and men—a dreadful spectacle—upon the jagged rocks below."

When Marcellus saw the devastation visited upon his fleet, he is said to have exclaimed: "Let us stop fighting against this geometrical monster, who uses our ships like cups to ladle water from the sea, and has whipped our most efficient engines and driven them off in disgrace, and with the uncanny jugglery of his mind has outrivaled the exploits of the hundred-handed giants of mythology." Finally the Roman soldiers had become so fearful, observes Plutarch, that whenever they saw a bit of rope or a stick of timber projecting a little over the wall they cried, "Here comes Archimedes," and turned their backs and fled.

Realizing the impossibility of conquest by assault, Marcellus decided to overcome the Syracusans by means of a blockade. Yet in spite of this blockade the ingenuity of Archimedes held off the surrender of his city for three years. And even then it was only through the carelessness of the Syracusans that their city fell. It was on the night of the festival held in honor of Artemis, the goddess of the moon. The people of the beleaguered city had yielded themselves up too freely to their wine and their sport. Shortly before dawn, "when their senses were befuddled and their bodies worn out," a number of Roman soldiers succeeded in climbing over the walls and in opening the gates of the city from within. When the Syracusans awoke the next morning, they found their city in the hands of the enemy.

As Marcellus looked down upon the city from the heights just outside the walls, he is said "to have wept much in commiseration of its impending fate." For he knew that his soldiers, having been held so long at the leash, could not now be restrained from "their harvest of plunder." Indeed, even among his officers many were in favor of razing the city to the ground and putting all the inhabitants to the sword. To this riotous fury of revenge Marcellus vigorously objected. For he admired the courage of the Syracusans who had so long and so brilliantly held out against him. He especially admired his "geometrical" opponent. "Let no one," he commanded, "dare to lay a violent hand upon Archimedes. This man shall be our personal guest."

III

AS FOR ARCHIMEDES, he was sitting quietly in the market place drawing a circle in the sand and calculating some abstruse mathematical problem. So wrapped up was he in his thought that he was surprised to see a drunken Roman soldier rush upon him with his sword. "Before you kill me, my friend," said Archimedes, "pray let me finish my circle."

But the soldier paid no heed to him and transfixed him with his sword.

"Ah well," whispered the gentle old scientist as he lay dying upon the ground, "they've taken away my body, but I shall take away my mind."

ROGER BACON

Great Scientific Contributions by Roger Bacon

Experiments in magnetism, optics, gunpowder, poison gases, etc.

BOOKS:
Opus Majus.
Opus Minus.

Opus Tertium.
Compendium of the Study of Philosophy.
Compendium of the Study of Theology.
Metaphysics.
A Critical Study of Aristotle.

Roger Bacon

Roger Bacon

1214–1294

H<small>E DID NOT CAUSE</small> a great stir in the world of his contemporaries. He was one of nature's stepchildren as judged by the yardstick of personal success. He lived to a disillusioned old age, having failed to see any of his dreams come true. And when he died no one noted the day of his passing.

Yet gradually as his name emerged from the forgotten manuscripts, and as the formulas bearing his imprint were unfolded to the incredulous eyes of the generations that followed, a world of legend took shape around the axis of his achievements. And the adulation heaped upon him after his death was as ridiculous as the disrepute inflicted upon him while he lived. The living scientist had been little more than a clown; the dead "magician" was little less than a god. "By the natural condensation of the air," wrote a scholar of the Middle Ages, "Friar Roger, called Bacon, made a bridge thirty miles long over the sea from England to the Continent; and then, after passing over it safely with all his retinue, he destroyed it by rarefying the air." Another chronicler of the fourteenth century declared that Roger Bacon had constructed two mirrors. "By one of them he could light a candle at any hour, day or night; in the other he could see what people were doing in any part of the world." It was further asserted that the little Franciscan friar had fashioned an enormous head of brass "from which he could obtain the answer to any question he asked." And the favorite utterance of this metal oracle, added the medieval scholars, was the enigmatic sentence: "Time is, time was, time is past."

Such was the world's distorted estimate of Roger Bacon over a period of several centuries. At last, however, the little Franciscan exacted from an erratic mankind the proper appraisal of his achievements. There is a tablet at Oxford, on the site of the *Grey Friars*—the Franciscan lodgings of the man whose works had been so amusingly misunderstood. And this, in part, is the inscription upon the tablet:

"The great philosopher, Roger Bacon . . . who by the experimental method extended . . . the realm of science after a long life of untiring activity . . . fell asleep in Christ A.D. 1292."

II

LITTLE IS KNOWN about the external events of Roger Bacon's life. All we have is the summary of his internal life—his ideas.

Bacon's unorthodox ideas came to him as a result of his orthodox training at Oxford. He entered upon his scientific experiments by way of protest against the unscientific attitude of his teachers. He felt that there was something wrong with a system of education which had inherited its metaphysics direct from Aristotle and which had formulated a series of blind dogmas about the heavens and the earth without a single scientific experiment to ascertain whether the doctrines of Aristotle were true. Such was the comatose state of ignorance in which the human mind had dwelt for fifteen hundred years. The majority of the so-called "professors of science" at the universities were nothing but learned doctors in mystical hocus-pocus. They were content "to do as Aristotle had done," forgetting in their foolishness that Aristotle had lacked the necessary instruments for the verification of his scientific doctrines. And so, like the ancient Greek philosopher, they combined their physics and their biology and their mathematics into a universal and tightly organized system of logic based upon their wishful thinking as to what was *best* rather than upon their exact knowledge as to what *was*. They did not school themselves to observe; they moralized. They believed that all matter was animated by a conscious aim. For example, they said that the planets of the heavens moved in circles, "in order to express their divine perfection in this perfect geometric design of God."

To a man of sense the ridiculousness of this antiquarian attitude was quite apparent. To a man of sensitivity the fame that was bestowed upon these "crystal gazers" into the past was downright disgusting. Roger Bacon was hardly thirty when he decided that he could never become a part of this system. The professors of illogic were arrogant, far too arrogant in their ignorance. A man must follow the path of humility, thought Bacon, if he wanted to search for the truth. "True knowledge stems not from the authority of others, nor from a blind allegiance to antiquated dogmas." Rather it is a highly personal experience—a light that is communicated only to the innermost privacy of the individual through the impartial channels of all knowledge and of all thought. "More secrets of knowledge have been discovered by plain and neglected men than by men of popular fame," confided Bacon to his notes. "And this is so with good reason. For the men of popular fame are busy on popular matters . . ." The true scholar must turn away from the schools. Bacon had arrived at a sound—and somewhat paradoxical—solution to his problems. He would look to his religion for his science. He would leave his academic position—he had been lecturing on philosophy for some years at the University of Paris—and he would become a Franciscan friar.

It is true that the gentle Francis of Assisi, the founder of the Franciscan order, had been distrustful of learning and had enjoined his followers "to think little and to do much." But like Roger Bacon, St Francis had harbored his suspicions not so much against the principles of scholarship as against the pretensions of the scholars. Spiritually, if not intellectually, St Francis and Roger Bacon were kindred souls. Both men were genuine Christians in a world that had largely forgotten the essence of Christianity. "I will conduct my experiments on the magnetic forces of the lodestone at the selfsame shrine where my fellow-scientist, St Francis, performed his experiments on the magnetic forces of love."

III

FOR THE REMAINDER of his life Bacon took no heed "of discourses and the battle of words." He followed the tendency of his thoughts and in these he "found his rest." Through observation he acquired a firsthand knowledge of the "entire natural kingdom." The medieval philosophers had hotly pursued the phantom of theoretical abstraction. "What others had striven to see dimly and blindly, like bats in the twilight, I investigated in the full light of the day." He called himself a "master of experiment." And his experiments covered a territory almost as wide as the world. There was nothing known to "laymen, old women, soldiers and ploughmen" of which he was ignorant. He worked with metals and minerals and made weapons of war. He studied agriculture and mensuration. He took note of the remedies and charms employed by old gossips, and he examined the books of magicians in order that he might be able "to expose the falsehoods of charlatans." Nothing that deserved inquiry escaped him. How else could a man ascertain the glory of God than by specializing in an intimate study of all His works both great and small? "Let no man boast of his wisdom, or look down upon the lowly, for they have knowledge of many secret things which God has not shown to those renowned for wisdom." Bacon's insatiable curiosity led him to the discovery of many practical facts. He computed the inaccuracy of the calendar employed in his day. He demonstrated the characteristics of the magnetic field. He studied the laws of optics and suggested the practicability of constructing eyeglasses that would prove "helpful to the aged and to those with weak eyes." (What a fanciful idea! thought his contemporaries.) He hovered "tantalizingly close" to the principle of the telescope. "I believe I have come upon certain laws whereby a child might appear to be a giant and a man a mountain. . . . Thus a small army might appear very large. . . . So also we might cause the sun, moon and stars in appearance to descend here below, and similarly to appear above the heads of our enemies. . . ."

He was interested in chemical analysis and left a strange note about his discoveries in this field. "I have produced an explosion caused by the bursting of a small piece of parchment that out-roared thunder and a flash that exceeded the brilliance of lightning." But he concealed this formula for his invention of gunpowder—for such it was—in cipher language in his manuscripts. He was afraid that the secret might fall into the hands of those who would do harm with so powerful an invention. It requires, he said, not only ingenuity but intelligence to employ the principles of science to human advantage. Man is not made for nature, but nature is made for man. "Look at things, try them, see how they can act on you, and *how you can act on them*."

But this, asserted the savants of his day, was sheer blasphemy—this searching into the secrets of God for the benefit of man. The Franciscans among whom Bacon had come in his quest for peace—even they at last had lost patience with him. Scientists who experimented with the works of God instead of accepting them with an implicit faith were nothing less than magicians of evil. The superiors of the order charged him with conspiring to produce "heresies and novelties" against the accepted traditions of mankind. They seized him and placed him in solitary confinement for fourteen years. When he was finally set free, just before his death, he was a man with a broken body. But with a spirit that nothing could break. "As for wealth," wrote this imprisoned sage on his diet of bread and water, "the true man of science neither receives it nor seeks it ... If he frequented kings and princes he would easily find those who would bestow on him honors and wealth. But that would hinder him from pursuing the great experiments in which he delights ... In his pursuit of knowledge the philosopher can remove even the walls of his cell to the outermost limits of the world."

IV

THE WIDESPREAD KNOWLEDGE of Roger Bacon had come to the attention of at least one man who appreciated it. This man was the pope. Some years before Bacon's imprisonment it had reached the pope's ears that the modest friar had discovered many answers to the "secrets of nature and many remedies for the physical ills of men." There followed a correspondence between the two men. The pope requested Bacon to "declare through your writing what remedies seem to you fitting for dealing with those matters which you recently intimated to be of such moment; and do this secretly as far as you are able." Whereupon Bacon sent him his manuscript, the *Opus Majus,* through the hands of one of his favorite pupils. But the roads were few and travel was slow. The pope died within a twelvemonth, before the manuscript reached him. The Holy See was plunged into a great political struggle with the German emperors and in the midst of the altercation no one found the time to examine the greatest scientific treatise of the age. The manuscript fell into complete oblivion for four hundred and fifty years before it was finally published (in 1733). No wonder Bacon had expressed his utter contempt for the judgment of his fellow men!

During the years of his imprisonment, however, his cynical contempt became transformed into philosophical aloofness. Little by little the conviction grew upon him that his confinement away from the bulk of mankind was more than merely physical.

It was the outward symbol of a spiritual cleavage between the man of original thought and the world of superstitious dogma. The real prisoners of life were not the thinkers whose bodies were locked behind the bars of iron, but the dogmatists whose minds were chained behind the bars of prejudice. He pitied his jailers for the confinement of their souls. "May God release them from the shackles of their ignorance."

It was this purpose that had animated his scientific investigations and his religious convictions. He had tried to liberate the human spirit through a more intelligent understanding of the eternal laws of the Creator. He had been accused as a heretic, yet he regarded himself as the most honest of believers. For he had tried to prove the validity of his belief—to fortify his *love* of God with a *knowledge* of God. He had pursued his scientific studies with but a single aim—"to reëstablish upon a firmer basis the divine teachings of the Church."

And it was for this service that he had been condemned to a "martyrdom of silence." Yet he was not completely silent. Toward the end of his imprisonment he was allowed to converse with his pupils. The results of many of his researches—such as his discovery of gunpowder and of poison gases—he had buried in the mystery of cipher language so that unscrupulous laymen might never utilize them for destructive ends. But the elements of his constructive philosophy—those "principles of peace" that were designed to lead to a better understanding between man and man—these he passed by word of mouth to the pupils who gathered eagerly around him. On one occasion he declared that in the course of a single year he could familiarize an intelligent student with the "whole pith of human knowledge." And to prove his contention he devoted himself with particular care to a lowly disciple, "Poor John," who spent a year with him in assiduous study and who in this short time "so widened his field as to amaze all who knew him."

And so he worked with his pupils, and clarified his thoughts, and prayed for the day of his release from prison. But gradually he became aware that it was already too late for his release. The end of the quest, and he was not yet eighty—a mere tyro in the classroom of ultimate reality. A single year to survey the entire domain of human thought, a whole lifetime to catch but a fleeting glimpse of divine truth. He had only glanced at the title page of God's manuscript, and now he must close the book. "A little groping toward the light—and then, the night."

Often through the gratings of his prison he watched the stars—cold and distant pinpoints of light mocking eternally at the helplessness of man. And yet at times he read in those stars a great and comforting thought. Some day perhaps the world might discover the researches of a friar in God called Roger Bacon. And the scientists would fashion lenses to bring the distant near and to focus the rays of truth to a clearer human vision. And then—who knows?—man might look upon his fellow man through the lenses of this magnified understanding and recognize him for his brother . . .

And Bacon's eyes grew luminous as he gathered his pupils around him and gave voice to his prophetic dream:

"I believe that humanity shall accept as an axiom for its conduct the principle for which I have laid down my life—the right to investigate. It is the credo of free men—this opportunity to try, this privilege to err, this courage to experiment anew. We scientists of the human spirit shall experiment, experiment, ever experiment. Through centuries of trial and error, through agonies of research . . . Let us experiment with laws and customs, with money systems and governments, until we chart the one true course—until we find the majesty of our proper orbit as the planets above have found theirs . . . And then at last we shall move all together in the harmony of our spheres under the great impulse of a single creation—one unity, one system, one design."

COPERNICUS

Great Scientific Contributions by Copernicus

Established the Copernican system of astronomy.
Reformed the calendar.

Books:

Commentariolus (Brief Commentary).
On the Revolutions of the Heavenly Spheres.
A Treatise on Currency.

Copernicus

Nikolaus Copernicus
1473–1543

FROM 1473 to 1543 a number of ambitious brigands were devastating the earth. The Sultan Muhammad II, Pizarro, Caesar Borgia, Charles the Bold, Suleiman the Magnificent, Baber, Francis I—these are but a few of the many conquerors who tried to erect a monument to their glory out of the murdered bodies of their fellow men. Today the names of these conquerors are all but forgotten. But three names stand out unforgettably from that period of military turmoil—Columbus, Luther and Copernicus. And these three names, it is interesting to note, are the names not of fighters but of seekers. Columbus discovered a new continent, Luther traced a new pathway to God, and Copernicus found a new answer to the riddle of the universe.

II

THE ORIGINAL NAME of Copernicus was *Kopirnig,* which means *humble.* And this word summarizes both the parentage and the personality of the "anatomist of the heavens." He was the son of an obscure baker in the Polish village of Thorn, situated on the banks of the Vistula. As a child he watched the sun as it "rolled along the heavens" from the glory of the morning to the glory of the evening. And at night he gazed at the innumerable little star-candles that lit up the circular ceiling of the heavens. He asked his parents to tell him about the sun and the stars, and they referred him to his uncle, the learned bishop, Luke Wassilrode. The uncle sent him books on astronomy, and Nikolaus devoured them and then turned to the more interesting story of the stars as unfolded in the open book of the sky.

When he was ten years old, his father died and Nikolaus was put under the guardianship of his uncle. His sorrow at his father's loss was tempered by the privilege that was now accorded him to dip into the many volumes in his uncle's library —books not only on astronomy but on literature and painting and sculpture and mathematics and music. He thus acquired from the first a catholic interest in all the arts and sciences.

At eighteen he entered the University of Cracow and came under the instruction of Professor Albert Brudzewski, one of the leading astronomers of the day. His uncle, however, advised him for practical purposes to turn his gaze from heaven to earth, and to take up medicine instead of astronomy as his life's work.

Accordingly he received his "doctor's cap" at Cracow and then asked his uncle's permission to continue his studies in Italy. The bishop generously gave his consent.

But before he started for Italy he applied himself for a time to the study of painting—in order, as he remarked, "that I may bring back my own concrete images of the beauties of that country."

And so, taking his brushes and his books, he went to Italy where for three years he devoted himself to his medicine, his art—and his astronomy. For he had learned to paint not only the landscapes of the earth but the constellations of the heavens. At the end of his three years of study (at the University of Padua) his professors "placed upon his head"—as we are told in the picturesque language of the day—"the two crowns of medicine and of philosophy."

But then he settled down neither to his medicine nor to his philosophy. Instead, he was appointed to the chair of astronomy (in 1499) at the University of Rome.

Here he spent four years—a period marked by brilliant lectures, widespread fame, and final discontent. His discontent had grown out of his habitual curiosity. He had been teaching his astronomy in accordance with the Ptolemaïc theory—a doctrine which placed the earth in the center of the universe and relegated the sun and the stars to the position of satellites that moved around the earth. This Ptolemaïc system had held sway for fifteen hundred years and seemed destined to hold sway forever. For it was based, maintained the savants, upon the "infallible" evidence of the senses. "The sky above us, as is obvious to anyone who looks at the circle of the horizon, is an inverted bowl. And the earth, as is equally obvious, occupies the very center of this bowl." Starting from this "self-evident fact," the astronomers maintained that the earth stands firmly in its place—an eternal queen to which all the heavenly bodies pay homage. The sun travels *over* the earth by day, and *under* the earth by night, while the stars travel *under* the earth by day and *over* the earth by night. The universe, in other words, "is a perfect sphere which makes a complete revolution around the earth every twenty-four hours."

But the astronomers had observed that this explanation of the universe was not so simple as it had appeared at first. For they noticed that some of the stars kept changing places in relation to some of the other stars. These "wandering stars" or "planets" seemed to have a motion of their own. One of these planets, which the astronomers had named *Venus,* appeared at times to follow the setting sun and at other times to precede the rising sun. A second planet, *Jupiter,* made a leisurely journey over the sky in twelve years. A third planet, *Mars,* made this journey in two years; a fourth, *Saturn,* took thirty years to complete the journey; and a fifth, *Mercury,* seemed also to move around the sky independently of the rest of the stars.

Then there was the moon, the eye of the night just as the sun was the eye of the day. This, too, was an "independent" traveler, making its revolution of the sky in about twenty-eight days.

Here, then, was the earth in the center, surrounded by seven heavenly bodies—the moon, the five planets, and the sun—each set like a jewel in a moving sphere of its own. And beyond and above them all was the vast and all-embracing sphere of the fixed stars.

This, in brief, was the Ptolemaïc system of astronomy—a succession of spheres fixed within spheres, and all of them rotating in different directions and at different speeds around the crowning achievement of them all—the earth upon which we live. "Man is therefore the center of all things."

But little by little, as time went on and astronomers became more observant of the skies, it became necessary for them to invent additional spheres and more complicated motions in order to explain the eclipses of the sun and of the moon and the occasional "capricious" migration of a planet out of one sphere into another. By the time of Copernicus the number of heavenly spheres had been raised to seventy-nine and their motions had become confused beyond the comprehension of the human mind. And then the astronomers turned to mysticism. Whenever a star or a planet seemed to be out of its proper orbit, they ascribed it to "a conscious intent on the part of the living soul" of that star or planet.

Such was the pseudo-scientific and semi-mystical astronomy as taught by Copernicus at the University of Rome. But after three years of this teaching he rebelled. In the course of his omnivorous reading he had come across various hints about a new kind of astronomy. Some of these hints dated as far back as Pythagoras, a Greek philosopher who had lived twenty centuries before Copernicus. "The center of the universe," said

Pythagoras, "is not the earth but the sun . . . The earth is merely one of the stars that turns around the sun." The philosopher Aristotle, to be sure, had ridiculed this idea. But from time to time, in the two thousand years that had elapsed between Pythagoras and Copernicus, a few timid voices had dared to reëcho the Pythagorean suggestion in spite of Aristotle's positive assertion to the contrary. This suggestion about the mobility of the earth had aroused the intellectual curiosity of Copernicus. What if a new system of astronomy, based upon their theory, were to explain all the eclipses, all the positions, all the motions of the heavenly bodies? It was an idea well worth examining.

But the examination of this idea would be the work of a lifetime. It required leisure and seclusion and quiet reflection. Above all, it required the abandonment of his teaching of a theory about which he now had his grave misgivings. The seeker must never presume to be a guide.

And so Copernicus gave up his professorship at the University of Rome and entered the priesthood in the Polish village of Frauenbourg. From now on, his life was to be dedicated to the advancement of the *Word* of God and to the contemplation of the *Works* of God.

III

THE NEWLY APPOINTED CANON of Frauenbourg didn't devote all his energy to his religious duties and his astronomical studies. For the poor of the parish needed medical attention, and Copernicus gave them generously of his time and his skill. His skill as a physician brought him so great a renown that sick people from distant countries came to him for help after they had been given up by their own doctors. And not infrequently the most distinguished doctors of Europe wrote to him for his advice as to the treatment of their difficult cases.

But even this did not exhaust the versatility of Copernicus. Not content merely with his spiritual ministration and his medical care for the parishioners, he looked after their material comfort as well. The village of Frauenbourg was situated on a mountain, and the inhabitants therefore were unable to secure running water. In order to get their water, they were obliged to go to the river which was almost two miles away. Copernicus resolved to "compel the water to come to the villagers instead of compelling the villagers to come to the water." Accordingly he constructed a dam which raised the level of the river and diverted its current to the foot of the mountain. Then he built a mill which by a simple and ingenious mechanism churned the rapid current of the river and raised the water to the level of the church tower. From this elevation the villagers received the water directly into their houses by means of pipes. In grateful recognition of this service, the community placed at the foot of the mechanism a stone inscribed with the name of Copernicus.

The name of Copernicus, indeed, had become synonymous with kindness. And wisdom. Whenever a new project was planned, for the benefit of learning or the betterment of life, Copernicus was called upon to offer his suggestions. At the request of his government he worked out a new system of currency, and at the invitation of the church he introduced practical reforms into the calendar. "Copernicus," writes Clavius in his monumental work on the calendar, "was the first to discover the exact duration of the year." (Actually Copernicus miscalculated the length of the year by 28 seconds.)

Having thus devoted his life to the threefold cultivation of pity and piety and wisdom, Copernicus became an object of esteem, almost of reverence, to a host of men and women.

Yet at the same time he incurred the hatred of some. Especially of the so-called Teutonic Order. This Order consisted of a band of robbers who, under the cloak of religion, plundered the clergy and the laity alike. When Copernicus dared to object to their depredations, they published a scurrilous pamphlet in which they charged him with the very thefts of which they themselves were guilty. Everybody, of course, laughed at their preposterous charges. But this did not faze the ruffians of the Teutonic Order. On the contrary, it egged them on to new and fiercer attacks against Copernicus. They tried to accomplish with their ridicule what they had failed to bring about with their rancor. They had heard that Copernicus was investigating the heavens with a view to determining the truth or the falsity of the Ptolemaïc system. Here was a vulnerable spot in the armor of their adversary. Accordingly they hired a number of clowns to go about the villages and to burlesque his astronomical studies. These clowns would gather a gaping mob around them and point out to them the immovable earth and the moving sun—"things which any fool can see." And then they would impersonate "the crazy priest" who "contrary to all rhyme and reason" maintained that the earth moved and the sun stood still.

The friends of Copernicus were indignant at this stupid and malevolent persecution. But Copernicus only smiled. "Let them be," he said. "The movement of the heavenly bodies will be influenced not in the slightest either by the ridicule or by the respect of these foolish men."

And so he continued to study the majesty of the heavens and became more and more convinced of the insignificance of man. And of the unimportance of the earth. This earth of ours, he began to realize, is nothing but a speck of dust whirling forever around the flame of the sun. Night after night he watched the stars from his mountain top and little by little he worked out that sublime theory of the heavens which to this day is known by his name.

And this, briefly, is his theory—a theory which so accurately accounts for all the inter-related movements and eclipses of the heavenly bodies that it is today accepted as a fact:

The sun is the center of our universe, and our earth revolves around it in a double motion—like a top spinning on its own axis and around a circular (or rather oval) track. This double motion explains the succession of the days and the nights as well as the rotation of the seasons. But the earth is not the only planet that spins around the sun. Other planets—Neptune, Uranus, Saturn, Jupiter, Mars, Venus, Mercury—are likewise carried "along the highways of the heavens" around this central star of the universe. And these motions are the result not of "capricious impulse within the living souls of the planets," but of the infallible and unchangeable laws of nature. Each of these planets revolves within its own individual orbit around the sun, never swerving from its course, and never deviating by as much as the fraction of a second from the immutable timetable of the sky. Every planet at every moment is to be found at its appointed place, every season arrives at its appointed time, and every motion of every heavenly body fulfills its appointed destiny.

Such, in the Copernican system of astronomy, is the unerring eternal clockwork of the sky. Get the key to this clockwork—the movement of the earth around the sun and of the moon around the earth—and you will be able not only to *explain* but to *predict* the relative positions of every star and planet at every given moment, the seasons in every section of the earth and the eclipses in every segment of the heavens.

It took Copernicus over thirty years to elaborate this theory of the heavens. And he worked out this elaborate theory not only experimentally, by means of his unaided senses—the telescope had not as yet been discovered in his day—but also mathematically, by the calculations of his precise mind. Patiently he checked his limited observations against his mathematical formulas—noting the eclipses of the moon in 1509 and in 1511, the positions of Mars in 1512 and in 1518, the locations of Jupiter and of Saturn in 1520, and the conjunction of Venus and of the moon in 1525—and in every instance he found that the actual phenomena agreed with his scientific calculations. And at last, in 1543, he was ready to declare to the world that the earth is not a stationary prison from which we are permitted to behold the journeys of the stars, but a whirling chariot in which our bodies are privileged to adventure over the open spaces of the sky.

And thus in the final analysis the Copernican system, far from belittling the dignity of man, actually glorified it. For in "liberating" his body it also liberated his mind. It gave wings to his imagination and aroused his intellectual appetite. In the world of philosophy, and especially in the realm of science, the work of Copernicus marks the beginning of the Modern Age.

IV

WHILE Copernicus was at work on his astronomical theory he corresponded about it with the leading scientists of Europe. But again and again he hesitated to publish the results of his studies —believing, as he wrote to the pope, that it would be wise "to follow the example of the Pythagoreans who left nothing in writing but communicated their observations orally, and then only to those who were intelligent enough to understand them."

In this hesitation Copernicus displayed perhaps a greater degree of prudence than of patience. It is probable that for a long time he was afraid to publish the book—not, however, because of the peril to his life but because of the danger to his theory. Unless and until he could substantiate his theory with a sufficient support of corroborative evidence, he felt that he would be merely bringing a premature idea into a hostile world. He dreaded to see this precious idea of his destroyed before ever it had a chance to become established. Finally, however, his evidence was complete and he was ready to present his new system of the world—"not as a hypothesis but as a fact."

Too old to attend to the publication of the book himself—he had now passed his sixty-ninth year—Copernicus entrusted it to his friend, Tidemann Gysius, the bishop of Culm. The book was issued in the spring of 1543. And it had a strange and anonymous preface. "This book," wrote the unknown "apologist" for Copernicus, "is written to present not a scientific fact but a playful fancy."

When the book came off the press, Copernicus was unable to object to this pitiable travesty of his life's work. For he was already at death's door. His body had been paralyzed some weeks earlier. He died (May 24, 1543) a few days after the publication of his deathless work.

GALILEO

Great Scientific Contributions by Galileo

Experiments in magnetism, gravitation, motion, etc.

INVENTIONS:
Compass.
Thermometer.
Improved telescope

BOOKS:
The Messenger of the Stars.
On the Solar Spots.
On the Nature of Comets.
The Laws of Motion.
Dialogue on the New Science.
The Two Greatest Systems of the World.

Galileo

Galileo Galilei

1564–1642

A YOUNG MEDICAL STUDENT at Pisa was kneeling in the Cathedral. There was silence over the vast auditory save for the annoying rattle of a chain. A sacristan had just filled a hanging oil lamp and had carelessly left it swinging in the air. The tick-tack of the swinging chain interrupted the student's prayer and started him upon a train of thought that was far removed from his devotions.

Suddenly he jumped to his feet, to the amazement of the other worshipers. A flash of light had descended upon him in the rhythm of the swinging lamp. It seemed to him that this rhythm was regular, and that the pendulum of the rattling chain was taking exactly the same time in each of its oscillations although the distance of these oscillations was constantly becoming less and less.

Was this evidence of his senses correct? If so, he had hit upon a miracle. He must rush home and find out immediately whether he had suffered an illusion or discovered one of the great truths of nature.

When he arrived home, he hunted up two threads of the same length and attached them to two pieces of lead of the same weight. He then tied the other ends of the threads to separate nails and was ready for his experiment. He asked his godfather, Muzio Tedaldi, to help him in this experiment. "I want you to count the motions of one of the threads while I count the motions of the other."

The old man shrugged his shoulders. "Another of Galileo's crazy ideas," he mumbled to himself. But he agreed to help.

Galileo took the two pendulums, drew one of them to a distance of four hands' breadth and the other to a distance of two hands' breadth from the perpendicular, and then let them go simultaneously. The two men counted the oscillations of the two threads, and then compared notes. The total was exactly the same—one hundred counts in each case. The two threads, in spite of the great difference in their starting points, had arrived at the same point at the same time.

And thus, in the swinging motion of a cathedral oil lamp, Galileo had discovered the rhythmic principle of nature which today is applied in the counting of the human pulse, the measurement of time on the clock, the eclipses of the sun and the movement of the stars.

II

GALILEO was always experimenting. Even as a child he refused to rely upon the authority of others. He submitted everything to the scrutiny of his own senses and his own mind. The son of a music master, he showed almost from infancy an interest in "the music of the spheres." His father referred to him as an absent-minded little stargazer who saw strange visions and heard uncanny sounds. At school, when the teacher was trying to explain the importance of the Latin preposition or of the Italian verb, young Galileo's mind was floating amongst the clouds in the wake of the toy balloon which his father had bought him as a birthday present. In his playtime he constructed all sorts of crude little instruments resembling carts and mills and boats—

anything that his unusually keen senses had observed in his daily walks.

At the age of twelve he was sent to the monastery school at Vallombrosa, that "shady vale where pilgrims leave their soul in a kiss." Here, under the influence of the Benedictine monks, Galileo flirted for a time with the thought of entering the religious order. But his father discouraged him from this thought and removed him from Vallombrosa. He had other designs for Galileo—he wanted him to be a cloth merchant.

Galileo, however, had ideas of his own. He now insisted upon a scientific career for himself. He was eager to specialize in mathematics—a field which in those unscientific days meant a lifetime of obscure poverty. Finally the father and the son came to a compromise. Galileo entered the University of Pisa to study medicine.

And to plunge, secretly and heartily, into the study of mathematics. Under his medical textbooks of Hippocrates and Galen he concealed the works of Euclid and of Archimedes. And in his spare moments he conducted experiments with instruments of his own construction.

His professors soon got wind of his studies and his experiments. And they disapproved of them. For it was nothing short of heresy for a student to think for himself. All the scientific problems, the professors declared, had been finally and conclusively settled by Aristotle. Whenever a student dared to raise an objection to a dogmatic pronouncement, the professor would settle the argument with a citation from Aristotle: *Magister dixit,* the Master has spoken. And that was that. But here was a young student foolhardy enough to check the dogmas of his professors with his own observations. His recklessness must be curbed—for the good name of the university, for the good of his own soul. They wrote to Galileo's father about it, and the old musician warned his son to mind his professors and to stop meddling with the unknown.

But Galileo disregarded the warning. He had made a profound discovery—the fact that "the science of mathematics is the language of nature." And to the study of this language he was now ready to dedicate his life.

III

GALILEO'S PROFESSORS refused to give him his doctor's diploma. And so he left the University of Pisa—a reputed failure in medicine and a "crackbrained juggler of useless figures." But his skill in the juggling of figures had won for him a brilliant reputation among some of the leading mathematicians of Italy—Giuseppe Moletti, Father Cristoforo Clavio and Guidubaldo del Monte—men to whom he communicated some of his scientific observations and who honored him with the title of "the Archimedes of his day."

But the Archimedes of his day found mathematics a poor substitute for medicine. For at that period many were sick, but few were curious. Galileo tried to get a number of pupils among the nobility, only to discover that hardly anybody cared to exchange abstract figures for concrete loaves of bread and butter. Fortunately, however, the chair of mathematics had become vacant at the University of Pisa and Galileo was able to secure the position—largely because of the fact that nobody else cared for it. For the salary was only 60 scudi (about $65) a year.

In order to increase his income beyond the starvation point, he began to practice medicine in his leisure moments. But his leisure moments were few. For he was now busier than ever with his experiments. It was his purpose, he said, to re-examine the scientific doctrines of Aristotle instead of accepting them as gospel truth. The way to arrive at a scientific truth, he maintained, was not to memorize the books of Aristotle, but to study the Book of Nature.

The students listened to his lectures with ill-concealed smiles, and the professors hurled anathemas upon his head. What did this insolent young upstart mean by removing from their shelves the sacred tomes of Aristotle and by replacing them with those ridiculous contraptions of pieces of string and lumps of lead and levers and circles and angles and planes? Why, these were toys for children and not tools for the serious study of the mysteries of the world. "Let him stop this nonsense," they threatened, or they would teach him a lesson he would never forget.

But he refused to stop his experiments, and therefore they decided to put their threat into execution. Contrary to the teachings of Aristotle, Galileo had asserted that two different weights released simultaneously from the same height would fall to the ground at the same time. This assertion, insisted the professors, was sheer nonsense. "Nobody but a fool can believe that a feather and a cannon ball will travel downward through space at the same speed." Now was the time to expose this absurdity, to the eternal disgrace of Galileo. They would compel him, in the presence of the entire faculty and student body of the university, to make a public exhibition of himself and his stupid theories.

Galileo was only too happy to accept the challenge. The place chosen for the "exhibition" was the Leaning Tower of Pisa. On the appointed day the professors dressed themselves in their long velvet robes and marched to the Tower. The students and many of the townspeople had preceded them. It was a noisy and hilarious crowd of merrymakers, prepared to see the execution of a man's character. Curiously enough, it had never entered anybody's head to verify for himself the simple fact about falling bodies. *Magister dixit.* Aristotle had spoken, so why bother to exercise your own brain?

And so the audience jeered on as Galileo climbed the steps of the Leaning Tower. In one hand he carried a ten-pound shot and in the other a one-pound shot. The moment came. Galileo released the two balls from the top of the tower. A shout of derision—and then a murmur of amazement. The unbelievable had actually happened! The two balls of iron had started together from the top of the tower, had dropped through the air together, and together had reached the ground.

Galileo had proved his theory. But some of the professors still maintained that he was wrong. In spite of the evidence of their eyes, they continued to advance the doctrines of Aristotle. And to persecute Galileo.

III

UNDISMAYED by his persecution, Galileo went on with his unconventional teaching—and his unconventional living. It was an academic rule at Pisa for professors to wear their robes not only in the classroom but on the streets as well. Galileo disobeyed this rule, since he looked upon it as utterly ridiculous. The robes, he insisted, interfered with his movements. Physically as well as mentally he wanted to be at all times free. "Conventional clothes, like conventional ideas, are the invention of the devil." Time and again he was compelled to pay a fine out of his meager salary for his persistent infraction of the rule. Finally the authorities of the university became impatient with this young rebel who dared to defy the established thoughts and customs of the day. He was not, they concluded, the right sort of man to guide the young. They must find some sort of pretext to dismiss him from the university.

And this pretext was not long in forthcoming. Prince Don Giovanni de Medici, the bastard son of Cosimo I, had invented a dredging machine with which he proposed to clean the harbor of Leghorn. A model of this machine was sent to Galileo for his examination and report. Galileo's report—which subsequently proved to be correct—was unfavorable. The machine, he said, was extremely ingenious with the exception of one item —it couldn't work. Incensed at this "affront" to his dignity, Don Giovanni demanded the dismissal of Galileo from the university on the ground of incompetence. The authorities of the university were only too ready to accede to his demand. The students, egged on by their Aristotelian professors, joined in the general chorus of yelping, and Galileo was hounded out of the University of Pisa.

But he had his friends—Moletti, Clavio, Guidubaldo, other mathematicians and physicists who had followed his brilliant experiments and appraised them at their proper value. With the help of some of these friends he was able to secure another, and better, position at the University of Padua. His salary was now almost $200 a year—a fabulous sum to Galileo.

But even more gratifying than the increase in his pay was the advance in his freedom. At Padua he was allowed to have his say without the interruption of catcalls and hisses. When he stepped upon the platform to deliver his first lecture (December 7, 1592) he was greeted with an ovation. Pupils and professors alike predicted a great future for him at this seat of learning where men were free to think. For Padua, together with the entire Venetian Republic, had been banned by the Church and was therefore exempt from the restrictions of the Inquisition. The Venetian scholars—and this included the faculty at Padua— were true to their Faith, but they insisted upon the principle of the separation of their scientific studies from their religious devotions.

It was therefore with a clear conscience and an unfettered mind that Galileo was now able to continue with his experiments. And these experiments covered a wide range of theoretical and practical knowledge—from the courses of the stars to the maneuvers of the battlefield. Although he had never served in the army, he had acquired a thorough knowledge of military architecture. And this knowledge enabled him to secure a number of private pupils—princes, nobles, soldiers—men who aspired to devote their lives either to ruling or to fighting. These private pupils, in accordance with the custom of the day, came to live with Galileo. Some of them brought their servants along with them. It was a merry and stimulating group that gathered around the table of this young professor of twenty-eight.

But it was also a noisy group. And at times Galileo was glad to escape from it—into the arms of the Venetian courtesans. These "honored ladies," like the famous courtesans of ancient

Greece, were regarded not as a vulgar class of "gold-diggers" but as a charming group of female companions trained especially for the purpose of supplying mental as well as physical diversion to their distinguished clientele. They could discourse intelligently on music, literature and art. They were invited to the banquets and introduced to the wives of the nobles. Their clothes and their manners were "modest yet seductive." They taught many a great lady of Venice how to take better care of her body and her mind. In their bath water they used aromatic plants. They anointed their hair, polished their nails and their speech and devoted themselves exclusively to the fine art of stimulating the senses of their lovers.

And Galileo was a man of susceptible senses as well as of good sense. He found great pleasure in the company of the courtesans. Especially of one of them—Marina Gamba. He never married— like Cicero he believed that a man can't be both a good philosopher and a good husband—but he took Marina into his house as his mistress and he became the father of three of her children.

His paternal obligations, added to the costs of his social diversions and to the expenses of his scientific instruments, proved to be a bottomless sieve to his inadequate earnings. Although his salary kept constantly increasing, he was never out of debt. At one time he was obliged to ask the treasurer of the university for a two years' advance in his pay. The treasurer granted his request, though not without displeasure.

And his obligations kept mounting up. The harassed young teacher of Padua had now another source of worry to contend with. His relatives in Pisa, having heard of his academic success, had come to look upon him as the financial pillar of the family. Their demands upon his purse were inexhaustible. His brother, anxious to enter the service of a Polish nobleman, insisted that Galileo advance him the money for his trip to Poland. This requisite sum was greater than Galileo's earnings for an entire year. Galileo borrowed the money and sent it to his brother. And then his sister, having fallen in love with a worthless young scamp, demanded that Galileo supply her with her dowry. Galileo borrowed one-third of the amount asked for, and promised to pay the balance at a later date. But right after the marriage his brother-in-law sued him for the unpaid balance. Another debt, another burden—and the demands from his family kept coming on and on.

Yet in spite of his burdens and his worries, Galileo found time for his amusements—dinners and dances in Venice; private musicales which he attended frequently as an auditor and occasionally as a performer, for he was an expert player on the lute; popular recitations and serenades and carnivals and burlesques. He even composed several of the burlesques and probably acted in some of them—broad suggestive farces written with little delicacy and much wit. For Venice at that period was a city of free thinking, frank living and boisterous laughter.

But these were merely the surface activities of Galileo's life. From first to last, his mind was dedicated to the pursuit of science. He organized, in a palace situated near the bridge of Santa Sophia, an *Academy of Refugees*—a scientific and philosophical club consisting of men who had "escaped" to Venice from various parts of Italy in order that they might be free to continue their studies and express their thoughts. It was at this club that Galileo first disclosed the results of many of his observations and experiments. He acquainted the members with the mysteries of the *magnet* and the magnetic forces of the earth; he explained to them the intricacies of the *compass,* a new instrument he had just invented; he demonstrated to them another of his inventions, a machine designed to raise water and to irrigate the soil; he showed them how to measure the temperature of the air by still another of his invented instruments, the *thermometer*. And finally he aroused their admiration with the most amazing invention of them all—the *telescope,* "a gazer into the distant stars."

For the invention of the telescope Galileo neither deserved nor claimed the full credit. On one of his visits to Venice he had heard that a Dutch optician by the name of Hans Lipperhey had accidentally chanced upon a strange discovery. As he was working on his spectacle lenses in his shop, this man had noticed that by placing a convex and a concave glass together he could make distant objects near. This accidental discovery interested Galileo. With his usual thoroughness he began to study the subject, to examine the curvatures and the groupings of various types of glasses and to calculate, by means of precise mathematical formulas, the visual results of these different curvatures and groupings.

Finally (on August 21, 1609) he was ready to make a public demonstration of the first scientifically constructed telescope in history. Followed by a crowd of his friends and admirers, he climbed to the top of the Campanile in Venice. And then one by one he allowed them to look through his "magic magnifying glass." To their astonishment they beheld "sails and shipping . . . so far off that it was two hours before they could be seen with the naked eye." They beheld "the traffic in a dozen harbors, the cattle grazing on the distant hillsides and the worshipers going in and out of their churches in the faraway towns and villages." And then at night, turning their gaze to the heavens, they beheld "the nearness of the distant stars."

Galileo was overwhelmed with orders for his telescope. But he presented it, without compensation, to the Duke of Venice. Whereupon the Duke, not to be outdone in generosity, ordered Galileo's election to a professorship for life at the University of Padua—at a salary equal in purchasing power to about $5000 a year.

Galileo had reached the height of his prosperity and his fame. Yet he was unhappy. "The wings of Fortune," he wrote in one of his letters, "are swift. But the wings of Hope are drooping." Ever since his arrival in Padua he had entertained the hope of returning in triumph to Pisa, the city out of which he had been hounded in disgrace. Again and again he had petitioned Cosimo de Medici, the Grand Duke of Florence (and of Pisa), to hire him as his court mathematician. He had even dedicated one of his books, *Operations of the Compass,* to Cosimo. But the Grand Duke had remained deaf to his petitions. And now that he had accepted his lifelong professorship at Padua, Galileo resigned himself to perpetual exile, the venerated prisoner of his fame.

And then Cosimo died, and his son Cosimo II, a former pupil of Galileo's, came to the throne. He offered Galileo the position which the famous scientist had so vainly and so ardently sought. Galileo broke his contract with the University of Padua and eagerly made his way to the court of Cosimo II.

And to the great tragedy of his life.

IV

THE CAUSE of Galileo's tragedy—and of his everlasting glory—was his epoch-making book, *Sidereus Nuncius* (The Messenger of the Stars). Galileo had written this book in the free atmosphere of Padua. And he was now confronted with it in the inquisitorial environment of Florence.

Galileo had printed his *Sidereus Nuncius,* as he wrote to his friend, Belisario Vinta, in order to "acquaint all the philosophers and mathematicians with some observations which I have made on the celestial bodies by means of my spy-glass (*mio occhiale*) and which infinitely amaze me ... I give thanks to God, who has been pleased to make me the first observer of marvellous things unrevealed to bygone ages ... I have ascertained that the moon is a body similar to the earth ... I have beheld a multitude of fixed stars never before seen ... Moreover, I have ascertained ... the nature of the Milky Way ... But the greatest marvel of all is the discovery of four new planets ... I have observed that they move around the sun."

And, he might have added, "I have observed that the earth, too, moves around the sun." But he failed to make this assertion, either in his letter or in his book. He merely mentioned it orally to some of his more liberal friends. To blazon it forth in writing would be tantamount to delivering himself into the torture chamber of the Inquisition. He remembered the fate of Giordano Bruno, who had been burned at the stake (in 1610) for his scientific declarations. Galileo felt that it would be safer for himself, and healthier for science, if he could continue to live and to conduct his experiments without the interference of the Inquisition. Together with the Koran he believed that "the ink of the scholar and the blood of the martyr are of equal value in the eye of Heaven."

But Galileo, in spite of his precaution, was destined to be a martyr as well as a scholar. For throughout the Florentine territory the Inquisition ruled with unlimited power and unflagging watchfulness. The Grand Inquisitor, Cardinal Bellarmine, had noted the fact that Galileo, while ignoring the question of the earth's movement around the sun, had nevertheless declared himself as a follower of Copernicus. Accordingly, on March 26, 1616, Galileo was ordered to present himself before the Inquisition.

When Galileo arrived at the Holy Office, Cardinal Bellarmine "advised" him to "abandon his heretical opinions about the earth and the sun and the stars." He was not to think such thoughts, nor to teach them, nor to defend them either orally or in writing, "under the threat of persecution."

Galileo, "with death in his soul," signed his renunciation and promised to obey. And the Cardinal released him with a triumphant smile. With a single stern decree he had stopped the planets from moving around the sun.

As for Galileo, he returned to Florence disheartened and ashamed. For a time he continued with his experiments in the quiet of his laboratory—and dared not disclose his discoveries to the world. But genius is born to be expressed just as the seed is planted to grow. In the long run, Galileo was unable to stifle his thoughts. He published another book on astronomy, and again he fell afoul of the dogmatic beliefs of the orthodox. Once more he was summoned to appear before the Inquisition—and this time on a far more serious charge. For he was now accused of "recidivism"—that is, the second commission of a crime after punishment for the first commission. The penalty for this "double crime" was death.

When he received the second summons to the Inquisition, Galileo was ill. The doctors issued an affidavit to that effect. "Galileo is in bed, and he runs the risk of going to another world rather than to Rome." But the Inquisitors were relentless. "If he is in any condition to come, let him be seized, bound in chains and transported to Rome."

He left for Rome in the frost of winter (January, 1633), and arrived there more dead than alive. When he presented himself before his judges he was in no condition, either physically or mentally, to defend himself.

His trial lasted six months. In the course of this trial he received the support not only of free thinkers but of many Catholic scholars and churchmen as well. For the Inquisition was as unpopular as it was powerful.

But the Inquisition had its way. On June 22, 1633, he was compelled to abjure his belief in the movement of the earth. "Before the Holy Sainted Gospels which I touch with my hands, I swear that . . . I reject and detest my former heresies . . . I confess that my error has been one of vain ambition and pure ignorance . . . I now declare and swear that the earth does not move around the sun . . ."

As his friends led him, trembling and exhausted, away from the tribunal, Galileo is said to have remarked under his breath, *"Eppur si muove"—But the earth does move!*

V

"IN THE MOST HOLY NAME of our Lord Jesus Christ, and of His Most Glorious Virgin Mother, Mary," wrote the Cardinals of the Inquisition, "we decree that Galileo's books be prohibited by

[47]

a public edict, and we condemn their writer to the formal prison of this Holy Office for a period determinable at our pleasure."

"Yet in spite of everything," exclaimed Galileo, "I shall remain a Christian!"

And a scientist. Although he had received strict orders to refrain from his scientific pursuits, he wrote another—and his greatest—book while he was in prison at Arcetri. This book, *The Laws of Motion,* was a summary of all the basic principles of mechanics. He wrote this work in secret, and had it smuggled out for publication in Holland.

Galileo never saw a printed copy of the book. For he had grown blind in his prison. But he enjoyed the comfort of holding the book in his arms as he lay on his deathbed (January 8, 1642). "I esteem this the most of all my works," he murmured. "It is the outcome of my extreme agony."

NEWTON

Great Scientific Contributions by Newton

Formulated the laws of gravitation.

Invented infinitesimal calculus.

BOOKS:

New Theory about Light and Colors.

On Motion.

Universal Arithmetic.

The Method of Fluxions.

The Mathematical Principles of Natural Philosophy.

Newton

Isaac Newton

1642–1727

HE WAS BORN shortly after his father's death—a puny, premature and sickly caricature of a child. The midwife who attended at his birth didn't expect him to live. "Why, he was so small I could have put him into a quart mug!" Such was destiny's whimsical way of introducing a prodigious mind to the world.

Newton's early years were spent with his mother. Then, by reason of her marriage, he was transferred to the care of his grandmother. At twelve he entered public school and boarded with a druggist. But he was a "poor boarder and mischievous knave." He was always up to tricks that kept the poor apothecary's wits in a panic. It was difficult to cope with a boy of such an unruly temperament and such unpredictable habits. He would collect small hatchets, saws and hammers of all sizes and build curious devices. He had become thoroughly acquainted with the mechanism of a windmill that was being constructed near the apothecary's house and he decided to build a windmill of his own. And it would be an improvement on all the others, he declared. He would run his machine with animal power! He would place a mouse on a treadwheel and deposit a morsel of corn above the wheel just beyond the desperate reach of this hungry miller. "Trust nature to set the mechanism in motion!"

He was always up to some trick of this sort. "Please, sir," he said one day to the druggist's brother-in-law. "May I have that box in the cellar to turn into a clock? I am certain you will never again be late through ignorance of the correct time." He built a clock whose hands were regulated by the action of dripping water that he poured into a pan every morning in the proper quantity. Next he built a "mechanical carriage" that was regu-lated by the hands and the feet of the rider. "Unfortunately, it could move only on a smooth level. It just obstinately refused to travel over the rough surfaces and ditches of the road." He took to flying kites and became interested in the "magic of sailing through the atmosphere." And one night he called his playmates together and told them with a devilish gleam in his eye: "I'm going to give the country folk the scare of their lives. I've just made some lanterns which I shall attach to the tails of my kites and fly them over the rooftops. People will think they are falling comets!"

Such were the amusements of the boy. In his more quiet mo-ments he wrote poetry and drew charcoal sketches on the walls of his bedroom. But his relatives expected him to be neither a poet nor an artist. They wanted him to till the soil for his liv-ing. He had gained a great deal of weight and stature, and he looked like a promising farmer. And so his mother took him away from his studies and sent him to work in the fields. Once every week she made him go to market with her servant in order that he might become acquainted with the "gentle art" of haggling. But whenever he approached the town, Newton begged the servant to go to the market and to transact the business himself. "You'll find me here on the way back," he said. "I shall be study-ing my books behind the hedge."

One day Newton's uncle became suspicious and trailed him on his way to market. He came upon his nephew stretched out in the grass, hard at work on the solution of a problem in mathematics. The old man shook his head with grave and majestic resignation. "Go back to your studies, Isaac," he said. "Either you're a great loafer or a great genius—the Lord alone knows which."

II

As the lad pursued his studies through Trinity College, Cambridge, he found himself possessed of a great handicap—mathematical knowledge came too easily to him. What comes easily, is easily despised. During his graduate work at Cambridge he not only anticipated the academic solutions of the problems but he frequently suggested to his professors newer and simpler methods of solution.

But the study of mathematics was of no special interest to Newton. He regarded this science merely as a rather indistinct pathway into the mysteries of nature. He was concerned with far greater mental conquests. For he was not only a thinker but a dreamer, not only a mathematician but a poet. His was the method not of the stodgy observer, but of the imaginative creator. It was his purpose to plunge boldly rather than to grope timidly into the unexplored forests of human speculation.

As a boy he had written verses expressive of a fundamental attitude that the years could never extinguish. One of his poems was entitled *The Three Crowns:*

> *Earth's crown, thus at my feet I can disdain,*
> *Which heavy is, and at the best but vain.*
> *But now a crown of thorns I gladly greet;*
> *Sharp is this crown, but not so sharp as sweet;*
> *The crown of glory that I yonder see*
> *Is full of bliss and of eternity.*

Thus spoke the poet who was willing to suffer in the fulfillment of his vision—to accept the crown of thorns as a prelude to the greater crown of glory. Every great scientist is a poet with a vision. But he is a special type of poet who seeks to interpret his vision in the scientific light of the spectrum. In his university lodgings Newton had constructed a chemical laboratory, and on the ground by his window he had planted a garden. The poet paced among the chemicals and the man of science walked among the flowers. Before he had reached the age of thirty his hair had turned gray—as if paling before the immensity of thought confined within his head.

And he gave full sway to his thought, taking the entire universe for his domain. First he peered into the heavens as his great dreamer-predecessors had done. He discovered the curious fact that there are different degrees of refraction among the different rays of light, and upon this principle he constructed a reflector telescope which was designed to bring the heavenly bodies to a brighter focus. He next investigated the nature of white light, since he suspected that it was merely a composite of all the colors in the spectrum. And finally he turned to his own little corner of the earth and studied the plants in his garden—the shapes of the stems, the texture of the leaves and the hues of the flowers— the magic raiment of the growing things that "outrivalled Solomon in all his glory."

As a reward for his efforts, Newton was elected to membership in the British Royal Academy of Science. And he was appointed—at the age of twenty-seven—to a full professorship in mathematics at Cambridge University. This appointment, to a mind of inferior caliber, would have meant a lifelong banishment into the nebulous dreams of academic hairsplitting. Cambridge was full of these men who called themselves professors and research fellows and who were nothing but "perpetual undergraduates." They were a queer lot, these research scholars. One of them, a "youngster" of three score and ten, had shut himself completely up with his books and vowed that he would never see the sunlight again. But at night he tottered down the stairs, leaning feebly on his cane, and made the rounds of the campus for exercise. He stared at the ground through dim-sighted eyes, and whenever he caught sight of a worm he jabbed at it with his stick and exclaimed viciously, "Damn you, you haven't got me yet!"

And even Newton, though he escaped the intellectual sterility of many of his colleagues, was not quite able to escape their eccentricities. Busy with his cosmic dreams, he had little time to look after his personal appearance. Often he entered the university dining hall with his neckband loose, his hose ungartered and his breeches unbuttoned at the knee.

Yet with all his untidiness, Newton was a young man with a romantic heart. On one occasion "the flame of a breathless passion" prompted him to propose to a young lady of his acquaintance. Tenderly he held her hand and looked into her eyes. But at the critical moment his mind wandered into other fields of thought. He had become absorbed in the binomial theorem for infinite quantities. Dreamily he grasped his sweetheart's finger— in his fit of abstraction he took it for his pipe-cleaner—and tried to ram it up the stem of his pipe. Awakened by her cry of pain he apologized sheepishly. "Ah, my dear, I beg your pardon! I see it will not do! I am afraid I am doomed to remain a bachelor."

He had few students in his classes. When he tried to teach his latest discovery, the infinitesimal calculus, his class shuddered at the novelty and the complexity of the subject and stayed away from the formidable individual who had "foisted it upon the world." His fellow teachers were amazed at the facility of his computations. He had discovered a method—and that as a mere student—for the evaluation of infinity. By means of this "secret method" he had computed the area of a hyperbola to "two hundred and fifty figures." But he hadn't bothered to make his formula public. Living as he did in the subjective realm of his fancy, he never dreamed of the sensation his discovery might produce upon other people. Mathematics was but a game for his personal amusement, and not an instrument for practical use. For Newton had a queer sense of practical values. Once a visitor asked him to appraise the worth of a prism. Fascinated with the prism as an object of scientific research, he replied unhesitatingly: "The value is so great I can not even ascertain it." Whereupon the visitor offered to sell the prism to him—at an exorbitant price. Newton accepted the offer. "Why, you silly man," exclaimed his housekeeper when she saw the purchase. "You need only have paid a price according to the weight of the glass!"

The weight of the glass! He was baffled at the weights and the values set upon things by other people. On what principles of logic did they measure, buy and sell? Often on his vacations he would return to his mother's home and sit for many hours in her garden meditating upon the strangeness of the world. And once, as had happened so often before, an apple fell accidentally from a nearby tree. It marked one of the turning points in the history of human thought, this casual fall of an apple to the ground. For it set the mind of the man seated in the garden spinning as dizzily as the earth. Here was the true value of things—a value that the appraisers of gems and the merchants of gold had never even dreamed of! It took the moonstruck poets, the only sane among the insane, to interpret aright the riddle of the universe.

And this is how Newton interpreted the riddle of the falling apple: *The law of the universe is the attraction of mass to mass.* In a crude and fragmentary form this law had been recognized for some time. People knew that weights fall to the earth because of the gravity at the center. But they did not know that this principle of gravity applies not only to the earth but to the entire universe. From planet to planet and star to star, throughout the incalculable terrain of space, this interplay of mutual attraction keeps every particle of the universe rolling over its appointed orbit in its appointed time to its appointed place—a complicated system of motion obeying the simple law of gravity under the watchful eye of the Eternal.

Newton returned to Cambridge in order to formulate this simple key to the riddle of the universe. As a result of his leisurely observation of the unimportant little things of his daily life, he had made one of the most important discoveries of history. He had raised the province of the physicist to the comprehensive plane of the astronomer and he had directed the imagination of man from the fall of an apple to the movement of the stars.

III

AT FIRST Newton was reluctant to publish the results of his observations. For he was a shy and retiring philosopher. "I'll print nothing," he had declared to his friends. "For that would only result in attracting acquaintances. And that is what I seek to avoid." His discoveries were a private pastime designed to amuse him in his solitary study. He was not bothered by a sense of obligation toward society. He was alone in a fanciful superworld of his own creation, trying to track down the footprints of the Eternal. It was a fascinating game—an excitement he wished to share with no one.

Finally, however, his friends convinced him that he owed a duty to his fellow men. And so reluctantly he began to prepare his manuscript for publication. He kept awake nights pacing back and forth in his study and refreshed himself for the long days ahead by a few hours' nap at dawn. "The meals that were carried to him warm for supper he would often eat cold for breakfast." A turn around his garden and then a sudden cry, "I have found it!" A mad scramble up the stairs into his room to make a few hasty notations while standing at his desk. An absent-minded saunter through the streets when he was invited to dinner and a sudden realization that he would be too late for his appointment. And then with a sigh he would go dinnerless back to his lodgings and resume the work on his theory. For hours on end he would stare trancelike into a telescope which he had mounted at the head of his garden. Sometimes he would turn with a puzzled look to the gardener whom he had overheard muttering, "This man knows more than the whole human race combined." The college librarian at Cambridge would refer to him with a significant motion of his finger toward his head. "A queer chap." He had few intimates, but rumor had it that he kept a cat. "Disturbed by her comings and goings," gossiped the librarian, "Mr Newton had a hole cut in the wall for her convenience. And one day, when the cat came down with kittens he resigned himself like a philosopher to the situation and cut a smaller hole for them beside the first one . . . But this," added the librarian, "is only a story. I don't know about it for sure."

Nobody knew much about Newton "for sure." Throughout his life his personality had been a problem too difficult to unravel. And finally, when the *Principia Mathematica* came off the press, the public found the book as difficult as the author. Even the scholars were nonplussed. A philosopher of the first rank called upon Newton and asked the scientist to suggest a course of study that might prepare him to understand the complex mathematics of the *Principia*. Newton graciously drew up a list of "necessary books"—an array so formidable that the philosopher in despair decided to give up his examination of the *Principia*. "The reading of the preliminary list alone," he explained, "would consume the greater part of my life."

Yet in reality, argued Newton, his book wasn't hard to understand. "The principles of my theory are within the intellectual grasp even of those who are unacquainted with the higher mathematics. For the book deals merely with the simple laws of matter." Every particle of matter in the universe gravitates toward every other particle of matter with a force inversely proportional to the square of their distances. "Do not be disturbed by my three volumes of geometric analysis." The essential attribute of matter is force—the innate power of resistance by which every body "endeavors to persevere in its present state . . . unless acted upon by some external force." This element of force —the tendency of the smaller body to resist and of the larger body to pull, the reaction and the attraction of matter—has transformed the static universe of the ancients into the dynamic universe of modern science. "Just give me the mass, the position and the motion of a system of heavenly bodies at any given moment and I will calculate their future positions and motions by a set of rigid and unerring mathematical calculations . . . I will calculate the tides and the motions of the waters and the earth. For the earth attracts the moon and the moon attracts the earth . . . and the force of each in turn tends to keep them both in a state of perpetual resistance. Attraction and reaction —reaction and attraction . . . The great masses of the planets and the stars remain suspended in space and retain their orbits only through this mysterious law of universal gravitation."

The leading scholars and scientists hastened to challenge this "outlandish" theory that the heavenly bodies moved in accordance with mechanistic laws. What a strange new divinity he had created with this mathematical theory of his—a machine-god without a will! And what a soulless sort of universe he had concocted in his "deranged poetical fancy"—a conglomeration of bodies whose only attributes are mass, position and extension! "This crazy mathematician," declared one of his critics, "will not have twenty followers in his lifetime."

And the prediction of this critic proved to be correct. Isaac Newton lived forty years after the publication of his book and his converts at the end of that period "numbered less than a dozen." But he remained unperturbed. It was with the utmost indifference that he had published his book in the first place. He cared little about the prospects of a general reading public and he made no concessions to the reader. At no point did he offer any clarification of his intricate text. Indeed he seemed to write the book with only two or three of his scientific friends in mind. It was to them alone that he addressed his arguments. "As for the rest of the world, it can go hang for all I care." To the criticism that the universe as envisaged in his theory was "the lifeless story of a planless mind" he replied: "The fact that the universe is so beautifully designed in accordance with such harmonious laws . . . must presuppose the existence of a Divine Wisdom, the hand of a Divine Creator." But he refused to be drawn into any controversy as to the nature of God. "I can frame no hypothesis about Him. I am a scientist and I do not speculate about theological matters. I deal not with God, but with His observable laws."

Few of his contemporaries understood Newton. But that was hardly surprising; the complex and paradoxical mathematician scarcely understood himself. At the very hour of his triumph— the completion of a cosmic theory that was to become the basis of all future science—he was a dreadfully unhappy man. For, ironically enough, he was anxious to be recognized as a second-rate gentleman rather than as a first-rate genius. It was not enough that he possessed a noble mind; he must try to acquire a noble rank. Again and again during the writing of the *Principia Mathematica* he begged his influential friends to secure him a political position with the royal court. It bothered him not in the least that the world did not appreciate him as the supreme philosopher since Aristotle so long as his countrymen would recognize him as a paid political retainer of the British king.

IV

IT WAS IMMEDIATELY after the publication of his *Principia* that Newton went into politics. At first he had shown himself a fearless opponent of James II when that stubborn monarch had attempted to stifle the freedom of the universities. At the overthrow of the Stuarts and the accession of William and Mary, he sat as a member of the Convention that debated the new constitutional order. By nature, however, Newton was not an orator. He spoke only once at the Convention during the great debates —and that was, to request an usher to close the window. The new king was not impressed with Newton's parliamentary ability. On one occasion, when asked to consult Newton on a political matter, William replied: "Oh, no. Newton is only a philosopher."

Yet the philosopher never relaxed his effort to become a courtier. And at last, when the office of warden of the mint fell open, Newton secured the appointment through the solicitation of his influential friends. His great mathematical mind was turned to the problems of coinage. The irony did not escape his countrymen. A character in a play remarked: "Newton? Oh ay—I have heard of Mr Isaac—everybody has heard of Mr Isaac—great man—master of the Mint." The name of Newton had become an object of ridicule from the lowest to the highest. "Some of my enemies," wrote Swift in exquisite burlesque, "have industriously spread the rumor that one Isaac Newton, an instrument-maker living near Leicester Fields, and afterwards a workman at the Mint in the Tower, might possibly pretend to vie with me for fame in future time."

This descent of Newton's from genius to mediocrity, remarked his more relentless critics, was only to be expected. To write the *Principia* had been merely a hobby with him. To become assistant master of the king's Mint had been his life's ambition. Newton had lost his sense of perspective, they said. His mind had broken down under the strain of writing the *Principia* and never again would he be "fit for mental service." Indeed, it was whispered that during the writing of the book "which neither he nor anyone else understood" he had suffered for a time a stroke of insanity. One windy morning, so the story went, he had returned from chapel and found that his cat had overturned a lighted candle on the table and set fire to many of his important papers. "Oh, Diamond," he had cried, "little do you realize the mischief you have done me!" And—continued the gossips—it was the grief at the loss of those papers, the result of many years of investigation, that had finally overturned his mind. "Perhaps too," observed some of the London wags, "he had caught a little touch of madness looking at the moon." And, indeed, some of his caprices were hardly those of a normal mind. "I must withdraw from your acquaintance," he wrote suddenly to a friend, "and see neither you nor the rest of my acquaintances any more." To another of his friends he wrote an apology for a letter he had sent him during a period when "I sat too often by the fire and was seized with a distemper." On one occasion he had severely criticized the work of his friend, the philosopher Locke. Upon receiving from Locke a letter of grieved expostulation, Newton replied: "I remember that I wrote to you, but what I said of your book I remember not. If you please to send me a transcript of that passage, I will give you an account of it if I can." Fits of temper, loss of memory, sudden outbreaks of suspicion and equally sudden outbursts of compunction—were not these the symptoms of a disordered mind? "No doubt all these rumors are exaggerated. But on the other hand, what else can you expect of a man who keeps constantly gazing at the moon?"

V

Now that he was drawing an adequate income as the king's servant, Newton felt that he must live in the proper style. He installed himself in the fashionable neighborhood of Jermyn Street, near Westminster, and took with him a favorite niece to become mistress of his household. His next job was to establish himself, if possible, as a "gentleman." Pretty embarrassing that his estate was so pitifully small. Yes, but he was the lord of his little manor, and he would testify on oath at the Herald's College that he was descended from the famous Newton family of Lincolnshire. "Can you trace the connection?" he was asked. "Why, no." Actually he could trace a connection only as far back as his grandfather, an honest but obscure farmer. But why despair? He would bolster up his shaky pedigree by attaching himself to an impecunious Scotch Laird. After all, it was not impossible to *buy* a noble pedigree. "Do you know," he remarked casually to a Scotch nobleman, "that I too am a Scotchman? My grandfather was a gentleman of East Lothian—or was it West Lothian? Perhaps it was my great-grandfather . . ." "Never heard of him," replied the Laird bluntly.

Ah, well, if he couldn't be a nobleman he could at least be a *rich* man. In addition to his city home he bought a country estate. Admiring scholars who came to visit him there discovered the "father of higher mathematics" engaged in the quite lower mathematics of disputing with his neighbors as to the number of cattle and sheep that he was entitled to feed on the village grazing grounds. Far from being immersed in planetary laws he was absorbed in haggling with his tenants over the price of repairing their barns and in threatening them with law suits if they failed to pay. The man who had discovered "the language of the solar system" was busily perfecting a language of violent invective against his ne'er-do-well nephew.

But he never quarreled with his niece, a woman of extraordinary wit and beauty. Indeed, there were rumors that he found in her a convenient advocate for the furtherance of his ambition. "When I was a young man," remarked Voltaire, "I used to imagine that the Court and the City of London had named Isaac Newton Master of the Mint by acclamation. But I was wrong. He had a most charming niece . . . She greatly pleased the Chancellor of the Exchequer . . . The infinitesimal calculus and gravitation would have been of no assistance to Newton without a pretty niece."

And at last—thanks again to the charms of his niece, it was whispered—Newton was knighted and introduced into the company of the Prince Consort, that "kindly, negligible mortal who drank like a fish." The now contented scientist settled down to a quiet old age of backgammon in the evening afterglow of a belated fame. But once more he was drawn into a stormy controversy. It had come to the ears of the Royal Academy, the learned society of which Newton was now president, that the aggressive German philosopher, Leibnitz, was claiming the sole credit for the invention of calculus. Newton's colleagues at the Royal Academy were outraged at the thought that a "foreigner" was trying to appropriate the discovery of a British mind. For it was Newton, they believed, who had first acquainted Leibnitz with the possibilities of calculus—"a method which Leibnitz had later perfected, to be sure, but had never invented."

The members of the Royal Academy took up the cudgels in behalf of Newton and England. The German savants, on the other hand, were equally vehement in their defense of Leibnitz and Germany. They lampooned the British as no scientists at all but as mere pseudo-scientists. "The British proclaim their discovery of an elephant on the moon when all they see is a fly on the end of their telescope."

Back and forth raged the international quarrel as to the priority of the invention of calculus. At first Newton tried to keep out of this quarrel. But finally, when even the British king had been drawn into it, Newton undertook to prepare a defense of his scientific reputation with something of the vigor he had employed in his effort to establish a family tree. But the controversy was as inconclusive as it was violent. Leibnitz went to his eternal rest, Newton returned to his backgammon, and the world accepted its calculus with a gratitude directed not so much to the ingenuity of an Englishman or of a German as to the genius of the human mind.

VI

As THE YEARS PROGRESSED, Newton lost his interest in the foolishness of controversy and the vanity of politics. His fame and his fortune were secure. Time now to look for the security of his soul—the final evaluation of his life not in the way of worldly success but in the measure of human achievement. He was finally convinced that he had been first and foremost a scientist. He had foolishly regarded his mathematical investigations as a pastime and his pursuit of success as the primary business of his life. He knew better now. "The value of life is not measured by the weight of its accumulated baubles of glass." The prism of the human mind is not to be exchanged for minted coin. At seventy-five he had learned to look through his telescope with a brighter eye. "Knowledge is an accumulation of vision" —the vision of the present superadded to that of the past. "If I have seen farther," he said with a humility he had not shown in his earlier days, "it is by standing on the shoulders of giants."

From this lofty eminence he was able to look fearlessly toward his own approaching end. Men die, as the stars and the planets die, in order to give birth to new energy, new planets and stars, new life.

And he listened to the music of the spheres as they whirled incessantly over their eternal course from life to death to renewed life. It was in this music that he finally lulled himself to sleep. Music, sleep, death, life—light. Aye, that was it! In his mathematical formulas Newton had somewhere caught and imprisoned this secret of the universe.

> *Nature and Nature's laws lay hid in night.*
> *God said, "Let Newton be!"—and all was light.*

LAVOISIER

PROPERTY OF
CARNEGIE INSTITUTE OF TECHNOLOGY
LIBRARY

Great Scientific Contributions by Lavoisier

Experiments and reports on magnetism, specific gravity, optics, sugar, starch, gunpowder, etc.

Discovered the composition of the air.

Laid the foundation for the modern study of the chemical elements.

Founded the science of chemistry.

BOOKS:

Elementary Treatise of Chemistry.

Physical and Chemical Essays.

Chemical Memoirs.

Lavoisier

Antoine Laurent Lavoisier

1743–1794

LAVOISIER enjoyed the blessing of genius and suffered from the blight of wealth. His genius advanced him to his glory; his wealth led him to his death. His ancestors had risen "from the dust to the stars." His great-great-grandfather was a postilion in the royal stables. His father was an advocate to the Parliament of France.

Like his father, Antoine prepared himself for the bar. His interests, however, lay in the field of science. He preferred investigation to litigation. So absorbed had he become in his scientific experiments that even as a young student he had cut himself off from "the frivolous pastimes" of society. He excused himself from his social obligations on the ground of ill health. And this excuse was not entirely without foundation. He suffered from chronic dyspepsia and lived for several months on an exclusive diet of milk. His friends advised him to do less work and to take more exercise. "A year longer on earth," remarked one of them, "is worth more than a hundred years in the history books."

Lavoisier agreed to remain a little longer on earth. He accepted an offer that would enable him to combine his exercise with his work. The famous geologist, Jean Guettard, had invited his collaboration in the construction of a mineralogical atlas of France. This meant an opportunity to travel, and Lavoisier was eager to grasp the opportunity.

Together with Guettard he set out for the Vosges Mountains in the summer of 1767. He had fifty louis (about $225) in his pocket, a good horse between his knees, his faithful servant Joseph by his side, the leading scientist of France for his master, and the entire world for his playground. It was in the highest of spirits that he rode off to his first adventure over the enchanted highway of science.

And his master, too, was in the highest of spirits—a state of mind, however, that was all too rare for Guettard. This geologist was as stubborn as a rock and as biting as the north wind. He went about with a perpetual scowl on his face against the "rascalities" of his fellow men. One day a candidate for the Academy thanked him for his support. "Don't thank me," snapped the old geologist. "I voted for your brain, not for you."

But toward his young collaborator the peppery old scientist acted with the severe tenderness of a father. "Lavoisier," he said, "has not only brains but character." And Lavoisier's refined but oversensitive character was grateful for the tender sympathy mixed with the occasional severity of his teacher. From infancy he had been too anxiously sheltered against the cutting edges of the world. His aunt—Lavoisier had lost his mother in his early childhood—had tried to bring him up like a rare and precious vase of fragile china. Even now that he was twenty-four, she followed his journey through "the mountains and mines of France" with a trembling heart. "Please let me hear from you frequently," she wrote to him in one of her daily letters. "I wait for the postman as for the Messiah . . . I fear for your health . . . the stifling heat . . . the dangerous precipices . . . the swampy forests . . . the wild beasts . . . Please be more careful even than you have promised me to be . . . and don't forget the ever-present anxiety of your loving friends."

It was a relief for Lavoisier to have escaped from these trembling hands into the care of a man who admired him but who refused to coddle him. Guettard toughened the mind and the muscles of his young protégé. It would have terrified Lavoisier's aunt to realize how exacting was the work that her nephew must undergo every day. Up in the morning at sunrise checking the thermometer and the barometer, recording the nature of the soil and the contour of the land, visiting the mines, the ironworks and the quarries, analyzing the river waters and the lake waters, collecting and classifying the various specimens of plants and minerals and finally compiling the results of his investigations in his notebook—such were the diversified activities of his daily routine. On his return home from his journey late of an October evening, he didn't forget to take the reading of the barometer before he consigned his tired body to the comforts of his bed. "The foolish boy will kill himself with overwork," wailed his aunt.

But instead of killing himself with his work, Lavoisier actually throve on it. He came back to Paris full of energy and confidence and grit. He entered his candidacy for the Academy and somewhat to his own surprise—for he was only twenty-five at the time—he was elected.

This was a tremendous honor, but it placed tremendous obligations upon his young shoulders. Either alone or in collaboration with other members of the Academy he was called upon to prepare scientific reports on all kinds of theoretical and practical matters—animal magnetism, specific gravity, the adulteration of cider, the Parisian water supply, the theory of colors, the extraction of oil from cabbage seeds, the manufacture of starch, the distillation of phosphorus, the decomposition of niter, the storage of fresh water in sailing vessels, the removal of stains from silks and woolens, the extraction of gold from the ashes of plants, the nature and the temperature of lava, the removal of the obnoxious odors in the Parisian sewers, the manufacture of sugar, the conversion of peat into charcoal, the respiration of insects, the rusting of iron, the composition of powder for fireworks, and hundreds of other similar subjects that were of interest to the scientific world of his day.

These activities were enough to give anybody a full-time job. Yet they formed only a small part of Lavoisier's labors. He had become associated with the *Ferme,* a company of "financial farmers" who collected the taxes from the people and paid a fixed sum to the government. The business of the *Ferme,* like every other kind of business, was a gamble. But it was regarded as a very *safe* gamble. The chance of profit was far greater than the risk of loss. It was always possible to squeeze out of the people substantially more than the government required as its fixed annual sum. Lavoisier entered this company of "financial farmers" because he wanted more money—not, however, for himself but for his scientific experiments. Personal greed was not one of his characteristics. But it was an unsavory sort of business—a gamble in which he was destined to win money and to lose his life.

II

IN THE COURSE of his work as a tax farmer Lavoisier met and married Marie Anne Pierrette, the fourteen-year-old daughter of the Farmer-General, Jacques Paulze. This marriage brought the addition of a handsome dowry to the already comfortably feathered nest of Lavoisier. And—since there's no better formula for success than a good pull combined with a good push—the young scientist-financier induced his father-in-law to get him still another job. He now held the triple office of *Académicien, Fermier,* and *Régisseur des Poudres* (Manager of the Arsenal).

Yet his triple accumulation of duties did not prevent him from attending regularly and conscientiously to his own experiments. For these private experiments he reserved six hours a day—from six to nine in the morning and from seven to ten in the evening. He had fitted up a laboratory in the Arsenal, and in this laboratory he entertained many of the leaders of the scientific world— Priestley, Blagden, Young, Watt, Tennant and Franklin, to mention only a few. He fitted out his laboratory with the latest and most expensive apparatus. And he hired as his assistants several of the more brilliant—and the more needy—among the younger scientists of the day. It required the greater part of his fortune to maintain this lavish "institute of experimentation." And out of this institute came the foundation for a science which revolutionized the life of the world. For it was Lavoisier who resolved the hazy mists of alchemy into the clear sunlight of chemistry.

III

WHEN Lavoisier began his experiments at the Arsenal, the chemical thought of the world was still wrapped in its medieval swaddling clothes. Chemistry was regarded merely as the handmaid of medicine. And a rather clumsy handmaid at that. On June 19, 1739, a British "chemist" by the name of Mrs Joanna Stephens received from the London Gazette a prize of £5000 for the publication of a "scientific remedy" that had "cured Mr Walpole, the Prime Minister, who had been suffering from the stone." This remedy was a pill concocted in part of the following materials: "Eggshells and Snails, a Ball of Soap, Swines' Cresses burnt to a Blackness, Burdock Seeds and Honey."

Other chemists, more methodical in their investigations but equally unscientific in their conclusions, conducted experiments in which they "demonstrated" that "one element can be transmuted into another element." One of the leading scientists of the seventeenth century, Johann van Helmont, described a "process" that enabled him to "transform" water into wood. "I took an Earthen Vessel, in which I put 200 pounds of Earth . . . which I moystened with Rain-water, and I implanted therein the Stem of a Willow Tree weighing five pounds; and at length, five years being finished, the Tree . . . did weigh 169 pounds and about three ounces . . . I had always moystened the Earthen Vessel with Rain-water . . . At length I again weighed the Earth of the Vessel, and there were found the same

200 pounds, wanting about two ounces. Therefore 164 pounds of Wood, Barks and Roots arose out of Water only." Previously to that experiment, van Helmont had converted wood into ashes and *gas* (a term which he was the first to use). Hence, reasoned this deluded chemist, water and wood and ashes and gas are one and the same element.

Still other chemists "demonstrated" that water can be transmuted into earth. They had noticed that when water was evaporated in a vessel sealed against the admission of dust from the air, a residue of earth was left at the bottom of the vessel. "Hence the earth is born out of the water."

It was this assertion that led Lavoisier to one of his first important discoveries. Ever since his journey with Guettard he had been interested in the density and the nature of water. He now entered upon a series of experiments in order to determine whether the residue of earth left after the evaporation of water was due to the decomposition of the water or to the erosion of the interior of the vessel. His scientific motto was not to rely upon speculation but to build upon facts. *Je veux parler des faits.* And the facts that he discovered as a result of his repeated experiments proved finally and conclusively that the residue of earth from evaporated water came from the vessel and not from the water. For in every carefully conducted experiment with pure water the vessel had undergone a loss of weight equal to the weight of the earth that remained in the vessel after the water had disappeared. "Water therefore is unalterable"—a conclusion that meant the final overthrow of alchemy, with its theory about the "transmutation of water into earth, earth into iron and iron into gold."

But this was only the beginning of his experiments. He went on to show that plants are not merely "quantities of water transformed into quantities of wood," but that they are compounds of various substances derived from the water and the earth and the air in which they live and upon which they feed.

Lavoisier's next step was to discover the nature of some of

these substances. He was especially interested in the composition of the air. A number of scientists, including van Helmont and Joseph Priestley, had already observed that there are different "kinds" of air—that is, different gases. It remained for Lavoisier to announce (in 1777) that the air consists of "two elastic fluids, one respirable and the other poisonous." To the respirable or *vital* fluid he applied for the first time the term *oxygen* (from the Greek words *oxys,* acid, and *gennan,* to generate). And now too for the first time he defined the chemical word *element*— Lavoisier called it principe—as "a substance that chemical analysis cannot resolve into any simpler substance."

Here, then, was the foundation stone for the entire structure of modern chemistry. Building upon this foundation, Lavoisier not only discovered a new chemical theory but also compiled a new chemical dictionary. Many of the terms invented by Lavoisier have become "the international vocabulary of the chemists" down to the present time.

And now came the final step in his monumental labor as a scientist—the publication of his *Elementary Treatise of Chemistry* (1789). Throughout the preparation of this book he had strictly adhered to the formula never to advance to the unknown except from the known, and never to deduce a definite result except from an observed cause. "I wish to speak only of facts."

The publication of Lavoisier's *Traité* marked an epoch in modern chemistry just as the publication of Newton's *Principia* had marked an epoch in modern mechanics. A few of the old alchemists scoffed at his "presumptuous ideas" and his "absurd list of thirty-three separate elements." They acted upon the antiquated prejudice that "everything that is new is not true and everything that is true is not new." The majority of the contemporary scientists, however, were prompt to agree that Lavoisier had opened up for them a new door into the mysterious laboratory of nature. "I am happy to see," wrote Lavoisier in 1791, "that my new theory has swept like a revolution over the intellectual circles of the world."

IV

BUT AT THAT MOMENT the tide of another revolution was sweeping over France. And it was getting ever closer to Lavoisier. The Father of Chemistry, having liberated the world from the Reign of Error, was about to fall a victim to the Reign of Terror. On January 27, 1791, he was subjected to a virulent attack in Marat's newspaper, *L'Ami du Peuple*. This attack, though it pretended to preserve the interests of the people, in reality subserved the interests of Marat. For this leader of the revolution had also aspired to become a leader of science. In 1780 he had written a *Treatise on the Nature of Fire,* and Lavoisier had expressed his opinion—an opinion that subsequent researches corroborated—that this *Treatise* was devoid of merit. Marat had then and there resolved to get even with Lavoisier. In his condemnatory article of 1791 he more than lived up to his resolve. "Citizens of France, I denounce to you the sieur Lavoisier, king of charlatans, companion of tyrants, pupil of scoundrels, master of thieves . . . Would you believe that this little publican, who boasts an income of 40,000 *livres,* is engaged on a devilish intrigue to get himself elected as the administrator of Paris? . . . Instead of electing him to this office we ought to string him up to the nearest lamp-post . . ."

Lavoisier paid little attention to this inflammatory article, believing it to be merely the discharge from the tumor of a wounded pride. But Marat continued his attacks, and before long he was joined by a number of other revolutionists who had caught the infection. They passed a decree to close the Academy of Science —of which Lavoisier was now the director—denouncing it as a "defunct repository of royalist thought." And when Lavoisier objected to this decree, they arrested him on the charge of treason against the new government.

Realizing, however, that it would be difficult to substantiate this charge, his enemies now accused him of a new crime—extortion as a tax collector. They searched his house, they seized his papers and—although they found no damaging evidence against him—they transferred him to the "prison of the condemned."

But Lavoisier did not lose his courage in the face of death. "I have lived a reasonably long and happy life," he wrote to his cousin, Augez de Villers. "I shall be spared the inconvenience of old age, and I shall leave behind me a little knowledge and perhaps a little glory. What more can anyone expect in this world?"

The trial was perfunctory. The chief witness against Lavoisier was one of his former employees, a convicted thief and forger. One of his advocates ventured to call the attention of the judges to Lavoisier's scientific work, only to be greeted with the caustic retort that "the Revolution doesn't need scientists, it needs justice."

Justice, however, was the last thing to be expected in the revolutionary hysteria of the moment. Lavoisier was publicly stigmatized as "a vampire whose accumulation of crimes is so overwhelming as to cry out for vengeance." And then came the climax of the tragi-comedy. Lavoisier was condemned to death on the imaginary and absurd ground of "plotting with foreign nations and the enemies of France."

He penned a final note to his wife. "Take care of your health, my dear, and remember that I have finished my work. Thank God for that . . ."

They took him to the guillotine on a May morning in 1794. "Only a moment to cut off his head," remarked Lagrange to Delambre, "and perhaps a century before we shall have another like it."

DALTON

Great Scientific Contributions by Dalton

Investigations in meteorology.
Disproved the false "science" of alchemy.
Established the atomic theory in chemistry.

BOOKS AND ESSAYS:
On Color Blindness.
The Atomic Theory.
The Molecular Theory.
New System of Chemical Philosophy.

Dalton

John Dalton

1766–1844

A LITTLE THATCHED ROOF in Eaglesfield, Cumberland Country. A sturdy Quaker father who won his living at the hand-
loom. A gentle Quaker mother, "Gudewife" Deborah, who lived
by the motto "for God and husband." Such was the environment
of the tiny infant born into the English winter of 1766.

The puny infant grew to be a stubborn, conscientious lad.
Once put to a task he would grapple with it against all odds with
the tenacity of a bulldog. Mr Robinson, the Quaker school-
master, often gave the boys difficult problems in mathematics;
and most of the boys, after a period of futile labor, would quit
and ask their teacher to reveal the answer. But Dalton was never
among the quitters. "Please don't help me, Mr Robinson. I must
do it myself."

Many were the heated disputes in the schoolroom as to the
best method to solve the problems set by Mr Robinson. One day
the boys placed a wager to back their convictions. But gambling
was poison to the sensitive Quaker conscience. "Ye shall not bet
money," commanded Mr Robinson—"but maybe candles."
Once this subtle moral distinction was laid down, John Dalton proceeded to win the bets and was thus plentifully sup-

plied with "farthing dips" of light. Always he sought for light.

At twelve he had acquired enough of an education, according to the standards of the village, to start a school of his own. Boldly he nailed a message to his father's door announcing the event. He, John Dalton, had opened "a house of learning for both sexes at reasonable rates." In addition to their learning, he informed his prospective pupils, he would supply them with "free paper, pens, and ink." This added inducement could hardly fail to attract notice. Paper, pens and ink were among the rarest of English commodities.

The school throve. The students were of all ages, ranging from "wee bratlings" to "hulking lads and lassies of seventeen." The little children sat on the knee of the youthful teacher and humbly lisped their A B C's. But the older students were far less docile. When the "principal" attempted to admonish them for their laziness they towered above him with a threatening look. "Want to go out to the graveyard and fight?"

At fifteen Dalton was tempted to give up his teaching and to go into "the agriculture business" with his uncle, a wealthy farmer who was very fond of him and who had no children of his own. But the young scholar soon dismissed his temptation. His elder brother, Jonathan, was conducting a Quaker school in the nearby town of Kendall. It might be a good idea to form a partnership in that school. Accordingly Dalton purchased an umbrella—for he was now "a grown gentleman"—slung a bundle of clothing over his shoulder, and trudged forty miles across the Cumberland Mountains to his new job. And to the greater glory of England.

II

THE BROTHERS introduced technical courses into their school. And to supplement their income, they assisted many of the townspeople in the running of their businesses and the writing of their wills. In that age of almost general illiteracy the pen was a

mighty instrument. John especially became an "object of wonder" for his "legendary culture." He took an active part in the
religious discussions of the townsfolk and he made frequent contributions to the farmers' almanacs. The unlettered people of
the Cumberland Country had come to look upon him as an
uncanny weather prophet. For he had begun to take a daily, almost hourly, reading of the weather—a practice which he continued for fifty-seven years until the evening of his life when his
hand was so feeble that he could scarcely make his entry legible.
He used crude, homemade instruments to measure the rainfall
in a country where "it rained every day"; and he sold these
instruments to the farmers so that they might make their observations along with him. He was very humble and very painstaking in the application of his "tiny human measuring rod"
to the "infinite patient plans of God."

He wrote enthusiastically to his friends at home about his
favorite hobby. He had observed that those who were entirely
ignorant of the matter supposed it to be a work of enormous
difficulty—a task beyond the means of anyone but a profound
scholar. "This, however, is a great mistake. A very little knowledge of arithmetic is sufficient for the theory of measuring the
rainfall." A very little knowledge and a great deal of humility.
For the raindrops of God cannot be measured by the instrument
of pretentiousness.

The Kendall "scholar" was indeed no scholar of booklore pretensions. He had read very little. He was merely a simple spirit
offering a recipe to other simple spirits linked to his own by a
common love for mental adventure. In one of his letters, written
to an "unlettered" girl of his native village, he prepared a table
of mensuration and then followed it up with an apologetic postscript: "Ignorance, no doubt, will look upon this as a trifling
and childish amusement . . . but . . . if to be able to predict
the state of the weather with tolerable precision, by which great
advantages might accrue to the husbandman, to the mariner,
and to mankind in general, be an object worthy of pursuit, that

person who has in any manner contributed to attain it cannot be said to have lived or to have labored in vain."

He undertook a series of lectures on natural philosophy based on his personal observations. He planned this series to include talks on "the laws of motion, color, wind, sound, harvest moons, lunar eclipses, planets and tides—subscription to the whole, half a guinea." But the lectures were not a success. People couldn't discern the dignified scientist under the homely demeanor of the country bumpkin. After a while he stopped talking to others and continued his work in silence. He roamed over the countryside, collecting many specimens of flowers and pressing them in his books with the object of selling them—since "they look pretty and attract the attention of the learned and the unlearned." He would fill a book of two quires for "half a guinea." But no one seemed at all impressed.

Yet undaunted he went on with his work. To his botanical studies he added a collection of common insects—especially butterflies and moths. "Some of these specimens may be thought puerile," he declared. "But nothing that enjoys animal life, or that vegetates, is beneath the dignity of a naturalist to investigate." He made experiments to observe the process of destruction in the vitality of snails, mites and maggots when they were immersed in water or deposited in a vacuum. And then he commenced to experiment on himself to determine the relationship between the intake of his food and the yield of his perspiration. But the world remained still unimpressed.

III

HE HEARD that in Manchester the Presbyterians had founded a college dedicated "to truth, to liberty, to religion"—an institution designed to serve as a protest against the dominant British universities which excluded Unitarians and Quakers. He applied for a position to teach natural philosophy and mathematics in this "school of dissenters." Largely because of "the lack of better candidates," he secured the job. But he found the academic restrictions of his new life unpalatable and decided to return to his private tutoring.

In order to meet his expenses, modest as they were, he was obliged to teach both day and night. Each day-student paid him ten guineas a year; and each night-pupil, two shillings a lesson. "And yet in spite of all this," he wrote with his unfailing good humor, "I am not rich enough to retire."

As a further aid to his early "retirement," he prepared a book on grammar. In this book the timeworn subject of English syntax was put under the scrutiny of a vigorous and original mind. The result was a work of fascinating highlights. And of fantastic errors—such as his listing of *phenomenon* as a *masculine* noun and of *phenomena* as a *feminine* noun.

The book enjoyed but a mediocre sale. But again Dalton remained unperturbed. He published a series of essays on his meteorological investigations with the prefatory remark that as usual he had relied not upon "a superabundant assistance from books" but upon his own observations. After the publication of the book he discovered that some of his conclusions had been forestalled by a French scientist whose work he had never read. "I am delighted," he observed with rigorous honesty, "that two people utterly unknown to one another have arrived independently at the same knowledge."

His own knowledge came almost always out of his personal experience. The principles of individual vision, for example— those strange laws which completely isolate one personality from another—were brought home to him in a peculiarly striking manner. One day he had bought for his mother a pair of stockings which he had espied in a Kendall shop window. His mother was delighted with the present, and at the same time puzzled. "You have brought me a grand pair of hose, John; but what made you fancy such a bright color?" Her Quaker instincts were shocked. "Why, I can never show myself at a meeting in them."

"They're a very nice sort of go-to-meeting color," John answered. Were they not of a dark conservative blue?

"Why, they're as red as a cherry, John!"

Dalton looked disturbed. "Strange, isn't it, Mother?" And then he recalled other similar instances. "Young women tell me they are surprised to see me in the street in a green coat. And I always answer that my coat is a dark snuff-red. Now who in the world is right?"

He was determined to investigate this curious inconsistency between his own vision and that of other people. Were there many like him? Were there more perhaps than the world suspected? Finally he found in Marysport two men—brothers—who confessed to a similar idiosyncrasy of vision. Yellow to them was the most conspicuous color in the solar spectrum. Rose and pink seemed to them to have an affinity with sky blue. They saw no difference between blood-red and green. These peculiarities coincided exactly with Dalton's own experience. Jokingly a friend had written to him: "I find by your accounts that you must have very imperfect ideas of the charms which . . . constitute beauty in the female sex; I mean that rosy blush of the cheeks which you so much admire for being light blue . . ."

As a result of this observation, Dalton formulated a theory to explain the strange phenomenon of what we call today "color-blindness." And though he never discovered the physiological causes of this defect, the powerful psychological lesson was not lost upon him. He had gone through twenty-seven years of his life seeing a world of certain colors only to discover by accident that the vast majority of his fellows saw a different world. But was his any the less real? This, henceforth, was to be the purpose of his life—to search for the reality that lay behind the contradictory evidence of our human senses.

IV

THE YEARS OF GROPING were over. He had decided upon chemistry, the realm of objective truth, as his life's work. For almost thirty years after his resignation from Manchester College he lived and experimented at the house of a generous clergyman, the Reverend Mr Johns. With his blunt and forthright honesty, Dalton had offered himself as a willing guest to his willing hosts. "One day, while my mother was standing at her parlor window," related the clergyman's daughter, "she saw Mr Dalton passing on the other side of the street; and on her opening the window, he crossed over and greeted her. 'Mr Dalton,' said she, 'how is it that you so seldom come to see us?' 'Why, I don't know,' said he, 'but I have a mind to come and live with you.'" And that was how it had happened.

His daily life never varied over the long stretch. His laboratory was his shrine. He generally rose at eight, lighted his laboratory fire before breakfast and devoted the entire morning to his experiments. He dined at one, "but always entered in much haste when the dinner was partly over." He spent his afternoons in the laboratory and retired from his work only to take tea at five, "rarely coming in until the family had nearly finished." After tea he repaired again to his "fire" where he worked until the supper hour at nine. After his supper, at which he ate a "methodical quantity" of food, he joined the family in the living room for an hour or two of pleasant recreation.

On Thursdays he took the afternoon off and went bowling on the *Dog and Partridge Green*. Methodically he played a fixed number of games, took tea at the inn and smoked his "church-warden" as he recovered his strength for the journey home. When the warm weather set in he conducted his meteorological experiments in the Lake Country and thus combined business with pleasure. He climbed the mountains not only to test his barometers but also to "bring into exercise a set of muscles which otherwise would have grown stiff." Often as he climbed with a party of friends he led the way at so brisk a pace that no one could keep up with him. On these excursions he took his food along in his knapsack—and was not averse to "mixing a little brandy with his water."

Periodically he visited his native village of Eaglesfield where he mingled with the yeomen and "had a real gude crack about the old days." As the years went on and he remained in the "blissful state of unmarriage," his friends began to inquire if he had ever thought of taking a wife. "I haven't the time," he told them. "My head is too full of triangles, chemical processes and electrical experiments to think of any such nonsense."

Nevertheless he was not entirely a stranger to love. He had become acquainted with the "handsomest creature in Manchester," he confessed in one of his letters to his brother. He had thought he was foolproof against mere beauty in a woman. But this was no ordinary woman. "She began . . . to compare the merits of Johnson's and Sheridan's dictionaries; to converse upon the use of dephlogisticated marine acid in bleaching; upon the effects of opium on the animal system, etc., etc. I was no longer able to hold out, but surrendered at discretion . . ." But then he concludes: "My captivity . . . lasted about a week . . ."

Other matters held him captive more securely. He was experimenting with the effects of heat upon gases, liquids and solids. He was surmising strange things about the chemical elements. The chemists of the period were making their tests in a midnight of uncertainty. Some of them had picked out a few stray beams of light here and there; but none of them had been able to hit upon any great universal principle that governed the various changes in the composition of chemicals.

To discover such a principle intrigued Dalton more than any affair of the heart. And gradually a momentous idea dawned within him. In the realm of physics Newton had demonstrated that the particles of matter were attracted by the weight of their atoms. Was it not possible that chemical bodies, too, might be found to consist of ultimate particles of atoms? To apply the atomic theory, the glory of physics, to chemistry would be a startling yet obvious innovation. Dalton could scarcely resist the appeal of his new hypothesis. He had found in his experiments that "in certain compounds of gaseous bodies the same elements are always combined in the same proportions." The ringing declaration of a fellow scientist never ceased sounding in his ear. "God ordered all things by measure, number, weight." Why should this not be true of chemistry as well as of physics? Why should the atom be the exclusive property of the physicists?

The possibilities of the theory were immense. Here at last was a simple principle fixing the proportions in which all chemical bodies combine. "If the relative weight of one atom to that of any other atom were known, the proportions or weights in all its combinations might be ascertained." Once a table of relative weights of these ultimate particles could be established the chemist would find himself in possession of the basic tools for his science. Such was the glory of the light that entered the methodical mind of the little Manchester Quaker as he toiled indefatigably at his test tubes. He struck the final fatal blow against the pretensions of the alchemists who had promised to transmute iron into gold and death into life. "Chemical analysis and synthesis," he declared, "can go no further than to the separation of particles from one another, and to their reunion. No new creation or destruction of matter is within the reach of chemical agency. We might as well try to introduce a new planet into the solar system, or to annihilate one already in existence, as to create or to destroy a particle of hydrogen." Or to transmute the particle of one element into that of any other element.

And now, having introduced the atomic theory from physics into chemistry, he proceeded to set up a table of the relative weights of the atoms that constitute the different elements. This table was rather crude. Dalton possessed neither the skill nor the exactitude of many of his followers. Moreover, his laboratory was far from being adequately equipped for accurate experimentation. But he had established himself once and for all as a lawgiver. Let the others attend to the details of the administration.

And—it must be admitted—he was not always tolerant of his more accurate administrators. In the notation of his formulas for the various elements, for example, Dalton had introduced a complicated system of circular markings. But when the Swedish chemist, Berzelius, ventured to substitute the simplified system of writing the first letter of the element with a number placed below to indicate the number of atoms in the compound—a method employed to the present day—the conservative-minded Dalton was shocked at the innovation. "Berzelius's symbols are horrifying," he remarked. "A young student in Chemistry might as soon learn Hebrew as make himself acquainted with them. They appear like a chaos of atoms . . ." In spite of his great discovery, Dalton was indeed color-blind.

And his generation looked on and marveled. What was this amazing scientist—a dull-witted plodder who had been chosen by God to give His law through a moment of supreme intuition, or a genius in the realm of thought, blithely unconcerned with the ordinary investigations of man? But, plodder or prophet, the quiet little Quaker of Manchester attended faithfully to his fire and slowly transformed the chaos of alchemy into the "order supreme" of chemistry.

V

HE WAS NOW FAMOUS. He had been elected President of the Literary and Philosophical Society of Manchester. And he had been invited to lecture at the Royal Institution in London. Here he met the great Sir Humphry Davy. "The principal failing in his character as a philosopher," said Dalton, "is that he does not smoke."

With the advance of his fame he had acquired an air of assurance that was as surprising to himself as it was to his audiences. "Nowadays," he wrote to one of his friends, "I can enter the lecture-room with as little emotion as I can smoke a pipe with you on Sunday evenings."

And so he went on his lecture tours with a cheerful heart and a confident smile. And with an open eye. He observed everything with the zest of a child to whom the world is new. Of Edinburgh he wrote: "This is the most romantic place and situation I have ever seen . . . The houses touch the clouds . . . In this place they do not build houses side by side . . . they build them one upon the other—nay they do what is more wonderful still, they build one street upon the other. . . ." He was especially fond of observing the ladies in his audiences—those who "wore their dresses tight as a drum" as well as those who "threw them around their figures like a blanket." But, he added, "most ladies look charming whatever their dress."

He enjoyed the contact of society and the savor of the convivial life. Indeed he was obliged to pay dearly for his too easy toleration of the cup that cheers the heart. For on one occasion he contracted a serious case of lead-poisoning from a bottle of porter in a London pub.

In due time he recovered from the poison of the beer and from the fumes of a too intense popularity. He was glad to return to Manchester and to his "comparatively obscure" way of life. After all, he wasn't a man of the world. Why pretend? At his lectures the fashionable classes of London had been shocked at his uncouth habits and his unlettered style. It was good to be back among the modest surroundings of his simple folk. In the busy world he loomed large and important. He had been elected to the Royal Society of England and to the Academy of France. In that world he must wear lace and preserve an artificial demeanor. Sir Humphry had presented him with the royal medal, and he had responded with a prepared and hollow speech. The atmosphere was stifling. Quakers just didn't take kindly to medals. It was such a relief to be himself again.

Yet the world wouldn't let him stay by himself. He had become a goldfish swimming in the transparent bowl of his fame. Everybody outside of Manchester must catch a glimpse of the "illustrious author of the Atomic Theory." The visitors came in droves to his shrine. Among these visitors was the savant, M. Pelletier, who in his grand Gallic imagination had tried to picture his meeting with John Dalton. Without a doubt this great Mr Dalton must be the wealthiest and most conspicuous citizen of Manchester, occupying an official suite in a large university dedicated to the pursuit of science—an institution somewhat like his own Collège de France, or the Sorbonne—a place of crowded auditoriums where Mr Dalton delivered lectures in advanced chemistry and bowed to successive waves of tremendous applause. Such was M. Pelletier's dream of John Dalton. When he arrived in Manchester he was jolted to find no clue as to Dalton's whereabouts. No one in the city seemed to have heard of him. After a diligent search, however, Pelletier was led to an alley and ushered into the back room of a small shabby house. He found an elderly man peering over the shoulders of a little lad who was "ciphering" on a slate. M. Pelletier's eyes almost popped out of his head. "Have I the honor of addressing M. Dalton?" he asked.

"Yes," answered the honest Quaker. "Will you kindly sit down while I put this lad right about his arithmetic."

VI

FOR A TIME nothing could lure Dalton away from Manchester. Sir Humphry Davy invited him to a polar expedition sponsored by the Royal Society with the backing of the Admiralty. This opportunity meant a goodly sum of money and additional fame. But Dalton declined the invitation. "The thought of quitting the regular habits of a sedentary life for a seafaring one," he wrote apologetically, "outweighs with me any inducement which the proposed scheme can offer."

Finally, however, he allowed himself once more to be lured into the world. And the temptress was the city of Paris. Here he met two of the most renowned of his contemporary fellow scientists, Humboldt and Laplace. Together, over the polite formalities of their social teas, these three scientists discussed the secrets of the heavens and the substances of the earth. Wherever he went in Paris, Dalton was lionized. When he entered the sacred precincts of the Institute, the president and the members rose to a man and bowed—an honor which had not been accorded even to the great Napoleon when he had taken his seat among the renowned "forty." Everybody pointed him out when he rode through the streets or walked into a public building. And throughout his triumphal procession in Paris he was chaperoned by Mlle Clémentine Cuvier, the only child of the eminent scientist. "Ah, she was a bonny lass!" he remarked long afterwards. "She treated me like a daughter."

When he returned home from his Parisian triumph, he put away his sentimental memories and renewed "the perpetual struggle of the mind against the stubborn fortress of ignorance." And as his years and his labors advanced, his friends began more and more to notice the similarity of his face to that of another great scientist. One evening an acquaintance by the name of Mr Ransome called on him and found him sitting with a cat upon his knee, a newspaper at his elbow and a plaster cast at his side. Mr Ransome picked up the cast and looked at it carefully. "I am glad you have had this likeness made of your features, Mr Dalton. Posterity will never cease to be grateful for this thoughtfulness on your part."

"But it isn't my likeness you're looking at," replied the chemist, much amused. "It's Sir Isaac Newton's."

"What a striking resemblance!" exclaimed Mr Ransome. "Indeed, I should call it a miraculous resemblance!"

"No miracle at all," smiled Dalton. "You see, my friend, it was the selfsame Mind that molded the features for us both."

VII

EVERY LIFE moves far too swiftly. A few anecdotes, one or two passages of laughter, a midnight flight of sorrow, and then the end. The Quaker in the somber stockings and the buckled shoes and the white neckcloth slowly tapped his way with his cane to the finish of the street, to the last dim corner where the future trails off into the nameless metropolis of the dead. He tried to halt his steps with medication in the hope that he might tarry a little longer amongst the people he loved so well. But his medicine proved to be of no avail. And his friendships were of no avail, and the distinctions of an adoring world. They had inscribed his name in shining letters upon the rolls of the scientific academies at Berlin, Munich, Moscow. And they had interceded with the British king to grant him a pension. And a fund had been raised to "halt his footstep in a trap of plaster" and to erect a marble statue to his eternal glory. A grim jest, this, for a dying mortal—a melting substance mocked by its solid shadow.

They completed the plans and selected the sculptor for the statue. They "took his profile as large as life . . . and then sketched a front view of the face on paper." They walked him through the apartment of the sculptor and showed him busts and statues without end. They gave him Tuesday for a holiday and told him he should see his head molded in clay on Wednesday. Already he felt that he had joined the ranks of the honorably embalmed.

When the statue was finished, he pointed to it sadly, *"There* is the great chemist, Dalton. *I* am only the hollow nonentity of a man."

He was seized with a paralytic stroke and partially recovered to return to his laboratory fires. But the fires of his life were going slowly out.

And one night, shortly after the completion of his statue, he tottered into his laboratory and groped for the books in which he had been recording his weather reports. Night after night for fifty years—the same rigorous attention to the selfsame humble task. Nearly 200,000 readings. He noted the hour—a quarter to nine. It was precisely at this hour that he made his nightly recordings. He picked up his pen. His hand trembled. He entered the reading of the barometer, noted the temperature, and then wrote in the final column: "Little rain this—" His manservant stood quietly by his side, waiting. Dalton's head nodded and he began to put down his pen. Then suddenly he shook himself awake. For he realized that he had not finished the sentence. Clasping the pen once more in his feeble fingers, he wrote the final word "—evening."

And the evening departed, and the morning came. But Dalton's eyes were closed.

HUMBOLDT

Great Scientific Contributions by Humboldt

Founded the science of natural history.

BOOKS:
The Kosmos.
Aspects of Nature.
Voyage to the Equinoctial Regions of the New Continent.
The Mountains and the Climate of Central Asia.
The Geography of the New Continent.
The New Species of Plants.
The Kingdom of New Spain.

Humboldt

Alexander Von Humboldt

1769–1859

HE WAS THE SON of Major von Humboldt, chamberlain to Frederick the Great. He passed his boyhood at the ancestral estate of Tegel, where he fed his eyes upon the miracles of the plants in his father's garden and his mind upon the miracles of the books in his father's library. Books of adventure—strange scenes in strange places—were his special delight. From early childhood he declared that he would devote his life to travel—to the study of the world and of all the wonders that it contained. One day a great man came to Tegel and had dinner with his father. He observed the precocious lad and questioned him about his interests. Just before he left he placed his hand upon Alexander's head. "My child," he said, "I believe you have a distinct talent for science." And then he turned to Alexander's father. "Herr von Humboldt, I would urge you to guide this child into the field of natural history."

"Thank you. I will do as you say, Herr von Goethe."

II

"ALL THINGS are engaged in writing nature's history." These words had stamped themselves indelibly upon Alexander's mind.

Everywhere he had caught glimpses of the writing in this universal book of nature. "The rolling rock leaves its scratches on the mountain; the river, its channels in the soil; the animal, its bones in the stratum; the fern and leaf, their modest epitaph in the coal. The fallen drop makes its sculpture in the mud or stone; not a footstep in the snow, or along the ground, but prints in characters more or less lasting a map of its march." Yes, and every act of man "inscribes itself in the memories of his fellows." But to read the meaning of the whole, you must travel extensively and experience deeply. You must go through the book of the world from the first page to the last, study every living species, observe every growing thing, examine every available specimen in the multitudinous handiwork of God. In Humboldt's day the science of natural history was as yet in its infancy. It had not kept pace with the immense progress made in some of the other branches of science. And Humboldt, now a student at the University of Göttingen, felt with regret that "whilst the number of accurate instruments is daily increasing, we are still ignorant of the height of many mountains and elevated plains." There had been numerous scientific expeditions, to be sure, but the leaders of those expeditions had been interested mainly in observing the external features of the countries they visited. "In order to know a country it is necessary to make a thorough exploration into its interior"—a form of scientific adventure practically unknown to the Europeans of the early nineteenth century.

It remained for Humboldt to take the first pioneering step in that direction. Born and brought up in a country which had no navy and no colonial possessions, he had nevertheless conceived a "violent passion for travel beyond the distant seas." Having completed his study of the little books in his father's library, he was now ready to open the bigger book of the world.

III

HE WAS BOUND for Mexico and Cuba in the corvette, *Pizarro*. It was the Spanish king who had given him this great opportunity of his life—to visit the Spanish possessions in America. The ship was plowing its way through a moody tropical night. The young scientist sat on the deck absorbed in thought. The moon broke fretfully through the clouds and scattered bits of light like amber marbles upon the waves. Humboldt had come a long way with his instruments. He had left his scholarly brother William behind in a world groaning under the hobnailed boots of Napoleon's armies. In front of him, just beyond the horizon, lay the mountains of the West Indies—the lookout of the New World. The waters whispered at his feet. The screech of a sea bird shot like an arrow through the air. Slowly the ship bells tolled. Death to the Old World. Hail to the New!

But there was death, too, on shipboard. A malignant fever had broken out among the passengers of the *Pizarro*. One of them was not destined to reach the New World. The bells were now tolling his requiem. The sailors sank to their knees in prayer as his body was lowered into the sea.

Passengers and sailors alike were relieved when the *Pizarro* finally reached the South American coast. Humboldt disembarked with Aimé Bonpland, a fellow naturalist who had come along with him. Together they planned to write "a scientific rather than a personal narrative" of their journey. "Amidst the overwhelming majesty of Nature and the stupendous objects that she presents at every step, the (studious) traveller is little disposed to record in his journal matters which relate only to himself."

Together the two scientists made their way through pathless forests and lit their evening fires to the sound of the *guachoro* (South American nightbird). They entered the caves in which these nightbirds made their nests and which were believed by the natives to house the spirits of departed men. They examined the curious plant of the *dragon-blood* whose white bark was stained with its purple juice. They tarried a while in Cumana where they had to be on their guard continually, to prevent the Zambos —half Negro and half Indian—from stealing up behind them and crushing their heads with their palm-tree clubs.

They then turned their steps toward Caracas and found a paradise of coffee-trees and sugar canes. Next they explored the wilderness of the Amazon and noted the *cow-trees* "which gave forth geysers of milk." They rode through stagnant pools alive with *electric eels*—dangerous creatures that swam under the bellies of the horses and would have sunk them with electric charges to the heart had not the natives vanquished them with their harpoons. They took excursions along rivers whose sandy banks were covered with crocodiles lying motionless in parties of eight or nine and basking with open jaws in the sun. Every year a number of the natives disappeared through those gaping jaws.

The two traveler-scientists hired a boat of Indian build and journeyed slowly down the *Orinoco*. In front of the boat's cabin sat the Indian oarsmen, two by two, chanting their native jingles to the rhythm of the oars. The hold of the boat was loaded with all sorts of animals and plants. When the scientists disembarked for the night they built a fire around their camp to keep away the tigers.

Throughout his travels Humboldt was particularly interested in the native tribes. He noticed everywhere a striking similarity in the customs and traditions of the different primitive races. "Like certain families of plants, which notwithstanding the differences of climate and locality retain the impress of a common type, the legends respecting the primitive state of the globe present among all nations a resemblance that cannot be overlooked." Wherever he went he found, in one form or another, "the selfsame substance of myths and fables" concerning the creation of the world, the flood and the regeneration of mankind.

"There is an underlying unity—a real science of universals—in the equation of life. *All life is one.*" This truth seemed to Humboldt to find its most vivid expression in the climate of the tropics—especially at noontide, when there exists a great calm of nature. "The beasts of the forests retire to their thickets; the birds nestle among the foliage or in the fissures of the rocks." Man too is at rest. But amid the apparent stillness of the hour there is a stifled sound, "an incessant murmur of insects." What an extent and multitude of living matter! Myriads of insects "crawl on the ground and flutter around the sunstricken plants. Confused sounds issue from every bush, from the decayed trunks of the trees, from the crevices of the rocks, from every nook and cranny of the drowsy earth." Thus does nature proclaim to man how under a thousand different forms life draws its united breath.

This idea of the unity of life had begun to fascinate Humboldt. From his observations of the multitudinous forms of life he now developed the elements of a world philosophy. In the thick recesses of the Jungle he had learned to consider man as of relatively little importance. "In this country of abundant vegetation whose growth no human agent cultivates or impedes, in this America where crocodiles and water-serpents lord it in the streams, where jaguars, peccaries, tapirs and monkeys fearlessly roam the forests which they inhabit as if it were an ancient inheritance"—in this vastitude of non-human existence the human race shrinks to desolate nothingness!

This, then, was the purpose of Humboldt's travels—to study the meaning of man in the mystery of nature. With this purpose to guide him, he continued his explorations from the *Amazon* to the *Rio Negro*. He entered into regions where he was compelled to battle his way against swarms of pestiferous insects. The natives were philosophical about this perennial plague of nature and made meals on white ants and on termites roasted in paste. In one of the settlements Humboldt found a Christian monk whose legs were so covered by insect stings that it was impossible to tell the original color of his skin. This man of God related sickening stories about the appetites of his neighbors whose omnivorous diet extended not only to insects but to human flesh. A short time before Humboldt's arrival in this settlement the chief of the tribe had fattened his wife and then roasted her for a public banquet. One of the Indians in Humboldt's canoe—a man of mild and engaging demeanor—casually remarked that he was a cannibal. He declared in animated sign language that of all parts of the human body he preferred the palms of the hands as the chief delicacy. This preference, he added, applied equally to bears. He was dismissed from further service.

Down the *Rio Negro* sailed the explorer's boat with its strange cargo. Many curious animals and birds had been collected and added to the "crew." Whenever the clouds gave warning of an impending rainstorm, these "sailors" got into a strange commotion. The macaw emitted frightening screams. The little monkeys scurried for refuge under the loose jackets of the men. The toucan beat against the bars of its cage in an effort to gain its freedom and to chase the fish that leaped to the surface in the approaching storm.

And now past the *Rio Negro* and back into the channel of the *Orinoco* sailed Humboldt and his crew. They reached the slope of a mountain where a huge rock, scooped by the waters of a thousand centuries, had been hollowed into a vast sepulcher—a cemetery in stone containing nearly six hundred skeletons of an extinct tribe. "Each skeleton reposes in a sort of basket . . . The size of each basket is proportioned to the age of the dead . . . There are some for infants prematurely born." Humboldt collected several skulls, the bones of a child six years old, and two skeletons of full-grown adults. Aware of the natives' superstition toward the bodies of the dead, Humboldt concealed the skeletons under his mule packs. But the subterfuge failed to deceive the tribesmen. Their primitive sense of smell, delicate as a dog's, betrayed the presence of the skeletons and aroused their resentment against the treatment of their "old relations."

[*104*]

One of the most interesting of Humboldt's experiences in this land of the "old relations" was a trip through underground caverns while the spacious *Orinoco* roared overhead. And one of his most gruesome experiences was a visit to the *Otomacs,* as savage a tribe as existed in those regions inhabited by the "Sons of the Devil." These men intoxicated themselves with a violent powder. They inhaled it through the nose with the forked bone of a bird and sneezed themselves into a fighting fury in their battles. And when there were no battles to be fought against other tribes, they turned their fury into the killing of one another within their own tribe. They rarely resorted to blows in order to kill. They merely dipped their nails in poison and "stung" their victims to death.

On through the broad expanse of the *Orinoco,* onward toward the town of legendary fame and fabulous wealth—*El Dorado.* The dream of every traveler. The fairyland of gold. Many of the early explorers had sought for it in vain. Sir Walter Raleigh had almost, but never quite, reached it. Always the natives told him it was but a little journey ahead, just beyond the horizon— and forever beyond his reach. Soon the name of the city had passed from its place on the maps into the realm of the myths. Yet adventurers kept still searching for that mythical haven— are searching for it to this day. For *El Dorado* is not only the city of gold, it is the vision of every soul's fulfillment.

> *Gaily bedight*
> *A gallant knight,*
> *In sunshine and in shadow,*
> *Had journeyed long,*
> *Singing a song,*
> *In search of* El Dorado.

Humboldt failed in his quest for *El Dorado.* But he had found the fulfillment of his song. He had now reached the concluding stages of his voyage. From South America he had traveled to Cuba and to Mexico, climbed the slope of *Chimborazo* to a height no man had reached before, taken sail for the United

States and spent a happy time at Philadelphia and Washington. And then he turned his eyes homeward. He had been gone five years—a period in which he had laid the foundations for Everyman's bridge to the *El Dorado* of his dreams. He had founded the science of a systematic natural history of the world. He was now ready to arrange and collate and bind together the book of life into a sensible unit and a logical plot.

IV

HUMBOLDT RETURNED to find himself one of the most talked about men in Europe. The rumors of his travels had spread like wildfire through every capital. Several times he had been reported dead. His brother William had waited anxiously for any news of him. And on a pleasant August day news came. Humboldt had arrived at Bordeaux and would shortly be in Paris!

His arrival was like the triumphal return of a victorious general. Much had happened in the political and the military fortunes of Europe since he had taken ship for America. The armies of Napoleon had met and conquered the strongest opposition that Europe had been able to offer. Empires had fallen, dynasties had collapsed and millions had died in Napoleon's quest for glory. Yet Humboldt's quest for knowledge had been equally potent in capturing the imagination of Europe. The "conqueror of human ignorance" had brought back from his "peaceful battles" a host of "prisoners"—specimens of botany, geology, mineralogy and zoölogy—the richest collection ever garnered from a foreign continent. Within a few years he had absorbed a lifetime of experience that would serve as an inspiration for all future naturalists—all thoughtful and daring and aspiring men.

And now he laid the plans for his mighty book, the history of his travels. To the preparation and the writing of this book he was to devote the bulk of his remaining years. This remarkable man who combined the body of the adventurer with the mind of the scholar could now retire into the seclusion of the cloister as cheerfully as he had formerly plunged into a jungle of tigers.

Slowly and methodically he examined the material for his book and divided it into six parts. In the first section he would relate the story of his adventures—with no other object than that of "preserving some of those fugitive ideas which present themselves to a naturalist whose life was spent almost wholly in the open air." Then he would devote a volume to each of the special branches of science—zoölogy, astronomy, physics, geology and botany. In addition to the main subdivisions he would include a political and moral history of the Spanish and the Portuguese in New Spain, and a sociological survey of the numerous tribes of natives in the wilds of the continent. The title for this gigantic work?—the *Kosmos*. For the subject matter embraced the entire universe in its scope.

Only one other man—Aristotle—had ever been able to accomplish such a comprehensive study as this. Humboldt realized that in this undertaking he would need the assistance of the greatest scientists of his generation. And immediately he set himself to the task of appointing and organizing his famous collaborators—the chemist Gay-Lussac, the astronomer Arago, the anatomists Latreille and Cuvier, the mathematician Laplace, the mineralogists Vauquelin and Klaproth, and the botanists Bonpland and Kunth.

At Arcueil, a village about three miles from Paris, the scholars met to discuss their plans and to share with one another the results of their individual studies. As for Humboldt himself, he prepared a number of books that were to serve as preliminary studies to the *Kosmos*. He wrote on the geography of plants, on agriculture and mining, and a preliminary narrative of his travels to the "Equinoctial Regions of the New Continent." The astonishing variety of his works moved even old Goethe to unqualified admiration. "He is like a fountain with many pipes; you need only to get a vessel to hold under it, and on any side refreshing streams flow at a mere touch."

His writings and his conversational powers had already gained for him, it would seem, a reputation that could hardly be brightened by any future work. Society looked upon him as "the high-priest" of the intellectual world. "Whenever he enters the room he replaces the puppet show of our former activities . . . He is like an elephant who can with equal ease tear down an oak or pick up a pin!" He was invited to lecture at Berlin. And in the audience was his intimate friend, the king of Prussia. He was appointed to the Privy Council and he was addressed thereafter as "His Excellency the Baron von Humboldt."

Yet Humboldt was still restless, still dissatisfied. He was sixty now and his hair was as snowy as the peaks he had scaled so long ago. But there were yet other mountains he must transcend. He must travel again. There were vast reaches of the world he must still explore before he could complete his studies for his monumental *Kosmos*. There were the fields of Siberia, and the vast reaches of the Ural Mountains, there were mineral deposits to investigate, tribes to visit, specimens to collect. He had spent almost a quarter of a century of research with the leading scholars, and here he was only at the beginning of his labors. And yet, was it fitting for a man of his reputation and years to shoulder a traveler's pack as eagerly as a lad of twenty?

His answer was in the affirmative. "To be a wise man is not enough." He must be "the wisest of men." At the invitation of the Russian Czar he set out on a scientific journey to the Ural Mountains. The Czar had given him a military escort for his safety, an expert cook for his comfort and an officer of the mines to assist him in his mineralogical researches.

They started from Moscow. At Nijni Novgorod they were joined by a nobleman who owned several large mining estates in the Urals. They passed through the country of the Tartars where they found a *Mollah* at prayer before the tomb of a saint. They offered him a seat in their carriage so that he might make the rounds of the distant shrines. Wherever they stopped, the *Mollah* performed his devotions while the rest of the company examined the ruins.

They reached an outpost of Mongolia and Humboldt presented the Chinese commander with a piece of blue cloth in exchange for a book on Chinese history. Informing the commander that his brother William was a linguist who would find the book valuable, he requested him to inscribe his name upon the fly leaf. The host graciously wrote "Chin-Foo"—and kept as a memento the pencil which Humboldt had handed to him for the inscription.

Humboldt sought for platinum in the Ural Mountains, he collected specimens of sea life in the Caspian, he measured the temperature of the sun in Siberia, and he studied the plants and the animals in the lowlands of the Russian steppes. Then he returned to Berlin after an absence of six months and a trip of eleven thousand miles.

Humboldt never left the capital again. He settled down in the *Oranienbürgerstrasse* near the palace of the king. He was a frequent guest at the royal court. Indeed the palace had become his second residence. No man in Europe was more celebrated. Or more happy. Yet his advancing years brought him pain as well as happiness. His brother William, one of the foremost of European scholars in comparative literature, had caught a severe cold while visiting his wife's grave and had passed away in Humboldt's arms. Humboldt would never forget the final words of the man who had been so much a part of him. "I shall soon be with our mother, and then I shall understand the laws of the higher world."

V

AT LAST Humboldt commenced his great work. He was past seventy and he was engaged in the writing of this book until his death at ninety. Like *Paradise Lost,* dictated in the evening career of a poet bereft of his sight, the *Kosmos* was written in the twilight career of a scientist bereft of his friends. One by one, like autumn leaves, they had dropped from the tree of life. An entirely new generation had sprung up—men and women who respected and loved him but who could not take the place of the old. It was in an alien world that Humboldt wrote his great epic poem of scientific research.

He was compelled to do all his writing at night. For in the morning he examined his notes, in the afternoon he received the constant stream of visitors who came to worship at his feet, and in the evening he dined with the king.

His life was a spring of ever-bubbling energy. And the harder he worked, the greater the demands upon his time. The world will not leave a celebrity alone, no matter what his age. He was invited to coöperate in every literary and political and social movement of the day. The king exploited his practical skill in diplomacy just as the scholars exploited his extraordinary genius in science. Writers of geographies relied upon his firsthand knowledge of South America. Students of economics sought him out for his thorough mastery of the fiscal system of Germany. The leading writers of the country came to him to kindle their own talents at the flame of his poetical inspiration. The compilers of German dictionaries consulted him for his great insight into the history and the meaning of words.

Yet greatness is but another name for modesty. Often in his later years he remarked to his friends: "You should have known my brother William. He was by far the more clever of us two." He regarded his brother as a real teacher and himself as a mere pupil.

And a pupil he remained to the end. On the cold mornings of midwinter the students at the University of Berlin would crowd into the lecture room to hear Bockh discuss Greek literature and antiquities. "We used to see in the crowd of students," remarked a future author, "a small, white-haired, old and happy-looking man dressed in a long brown coat." This man was Alexander von Humboldt, the "father of modern science," who came to "go through again what he had neglected in his youth." During the lectures Humboldt sat on the fifth bench near the window, taking notes like the other students on a sheet of paper. In the evening he attended the lectures of Ritter on physical geography. On one occasion, while discussing an important geographical problem, Ritter quoted Humboldt as his authority. All eyes were turned upon the white-haired scientist who rose slightly from his seat, bowed and then resumed taking notes. Whenever he was absent from the lecture room the students passed the word around that "Alexander has cut class today to take tea with the King."

Gradually his shoulders had become stooped. He was approaching his ninetieth winter. It was evident that all those who wished to see him had very little time left for their pilgrimage.

Bayard Taylor, the American poet, had come all the way to Berlin in order to meet "the world's greatest living man." The talk turned to American affairs. Despite the fact that he was busily engaged on the *Kosmos,* Humboldt kept himself at all times posted on current history. He understood American politics and American personalities. He inquired after Washington Irving. "He must be at least fifty years old," he remarked.

Bayard Taylor informed him that Irving was seventy.

"Ah," murmured Humboldt, "I have lived so long I have almost lost the consciousness of time." And his eye dimmed. He had lived long indeed. He belonged to the age of Jefferson and Gallatin. He had heard of George Washington's death while he was journeying in South America. He looked with a sad smile at Bayard Taylor. "You have traveled much, my friend. You have seen many ruins. Now you have seen one ruin more." He held out his hand to his departing visitor. This hand had clasped in friendship many of the leading personages of the century—Frederick the Great and Schiller, Napoleon Bonaparte and William Pitt, Goethe, Thomas Jefferson, Alexander Hamilton, Beethoven and Walter Scott.

Bayard Taylor paid a second and final visit to Humboldt the following year. In answer to his knock, the door was opened by

Humboldt's faithful servant, Seiffert, who exclaimed cordially, "Welcome back!" And then the servant added that "His Excellency" had been quite ill and that Mr Taylor would not find him as strong as on the previous visit. "But thank God his illness is practically over!"

Mr Taylor was ushered into Humboldt's study. The white-haired scientist was standing at a table which was covered with the proof sheets of a new volume of the *Kosmos*. "This is what I have been doing since you were last here," he remarked to Bayard Taylor as he picked up the proofs. "Several of the volumes have already been published. This one is just about to come from the press."

"Do you find yourself still capable of such exacting labor?" ventured Taylor.

"I sleep little," answered Humboldt. "Work is my life. The day before yesterday I worked for sixteen hours correcting these sheets."

Yet he admitted that he was unwell. With perfect scientific dispassion he discussed his physical debility. "He seemed to consider the body as something independent of himself," wrote Taylor afterwards. "He seemed to watch, with a curious eye, its gradual decay, as he might have watched that of a tree during his younger days of exploration."

He was very much absorbed in his memories. He told anecdotes about Alexander the First of Russia, and mentioned a trip he had taken to England during the trial of Warren Hastings. He related how in a single night he had listened to the speeches of Burke, Pitt, and Sheridan. Finally, as Taylor was about to leave, Humboldt begged him to pay him another visit. "You must bring your wife with you. I must be polite enough to live until then."

In the spring he walked arm in arm with the king through the quiet gardens of the palace, *Sans Souci,* built by Frederick the Great as a haven to which he might retire after the heat of his battles. But for Humboldt there was no haven of rest from his labors. Nor did he wish for any such rest until the fifth volume of the *Kosmos* was completed on his eighty-ninth birthday.

And the completion of his book meant the fulfillment of his life. Never did conqueror receive so generous an ovation from so great a number of people. Shortly after the publication of the last volume of the *Kosmos* the American Embassy at Berlin invited him to a celebration of Washington's birthday. The secretary of the legation offered two toasts—"to George Washington, the Father of his Country, and to Baron von Humboldt, the King of Science whose shoes no common kings are worthy of unloosing."

The aged scientist rose and in a feeble voice tried to say a few words. But hardly anyone could hear him amidst the general cheers. And then his friends, solicitous for his health, bundled him into a greatcoat and led him away.

In spite of his now rapidly failing strength, his friends boldly predicted that he would live to take part in a mighty celebration of his ninetieth birthday. But he told them that he expected to die in the spring. And when April came, the citizens of Berlin began to miss the familiar figure of the Baron strolling under the Lindens. "Where is His Excellency?" they asked one another. But no one could give answer.

Von Humboldt had taken another ship for a New World.

FARADAY

Great Scientific Contributions by Faraday

Experiments in electromagnetism, the conversion of electricity into power, into light, etc.

BOOKS AND TREATISES:
Chemical Manipulation.

The Chemical History of a Candle.

On the Various Forces of Nature.

The Liquefaction of Gases.

Researches in Chemistry and Physics.

Faraday

Michael Faraday

1791–1867

IN 1857 MICHAEL FARADAY had arrived at what most men regarded as the summit of worldly achievement. Professor Tyndall had offered him the presidency of the Royal Society. But "the most brilliant scientist of his generation" refused the honor. "Tyndall," he said, "I must remain plain Michael Faraday to the last."

These words adequately summarize Faraday's unusual personality. Throughout his life he declined academic distinctions and economic rewards in order that he might be free to investigate Nature's mysteries as "plain Michael Faraday."

And his origin was indeed of the plainest. His father was a blacksmith, and his uncles were grocers and cobblers and farmers and clerks. One of his brothers was a plumber, and the others too passed their lives along the obscure and unambitious level of their origin. But through some freak of nature—we regard as a "freak" any law of nature that we don't understand—the less than ordinary seed of the Faradays produced the one supreme flower of Michael's genius.

As a child he showed no promise of his future genius. An "average pupil in a common day-school," to use his own expression, he received but a scanty education in "the rudiments of reading, writing and arithmetic." His hours out of school "were passed at home and in the streets"—playing marbles, taking care of his baby sister, and "watching the sunsets."

His formal schooling came to an unexpected end because of a defect in his speech. Unable to articulate the letter R, he pronounced his elder brother's name "Wobert." Again and again his teacher, a desiccated old maid who loved precision and hated children, had tried to ridicule him out of this defect. Finally, when she saw that ridicule failed, she decided to resort to blows. Calling Robert to her desk—he was a pupil in the same class with Michael—she gave him a halfpenny and ordered him to buy a cane with which she promised "to give Michael a public flogging."

But Robert had ideas of his own about the matter. He pitched the halfpenny over a wall and then ran home to report his teacher's cruelty to his mother. Mrs Faraday, deciding that the children's health was more important than their education, took both boys out of the school.

In the meantime their father, unable to make a living in the Surrey village of Newington Butts, had resolved to remove his family to London—"the city of magic and miracles whose streets are paved with gold." Accordingly the Faradays adventured to the city and took up their residence over a coach-house in Manchester Square.

But the change in the Faradays' residence produced no change in their fortune. The family was still obliged to live on hard crusts of bread buttered with hope. Michael's personal ration was a loaf a week which his mother allowed him to portion out for himself—an excellent training for a future scientist. Every Monday, when he received his loaf of bread, he divided it carefully into fourteen sections—two sections per day, one for breakfast and one for supper. And thus through his careful "management" he never went altogether hungry although he never felt fully satisfied.

When he reached his thirteenth year his parents found it necessary to put him to work. Fortunately he was able to get a congenial job not far from his home. He became an errand boy to George Riebau, a bookseller and stationer at No. 2 Blandford Street. Mr Riebau conducted, among other services to his customers, a newspaper lending library; and it was the duty of Michael Faraday to carry the papers around to the customers and then to call for them when the customers were through with them. On Sundays he was obliged to get up before dawn in order to deliver the papers and to collect them again in time to "make himself neat" for the morning church services.

Mr Riebau's customers remembered him as a bright-eyed youngster, with a load of brown curls upon a head that "was always thrust forward to ask questions." This inquisitive forward thrusting of his head cost him a bleeding nose on one occasion when a door was suddenly opened outward against his face.

Mr Riebau's customers, however, were pleased with his services. And so too was Mr Riebau who promoted Michael, at the end of a year, to a "free apprenticeship" in bookbinding at his establishment.

This new job was to Michael a precious gift from the gods. For it enabled him to become acquainted not only with the outside but also with the inside of books. In his spare moments he read all sorts of volumes that came to be bound at Riebau's shop, and he saw a new enchanted world unfolding itself before his eyes. "I loved especially," he tells us, "to read the scientific books which were under my hand; and, amongst them, delighted in Marcet's *Conversations in Chemistry* and the electrical treatises in the *Encyclopaedia Britannica*." Guided by his reading, he made "such simple experiments in chemistry as could be defrayed in their expense by a few pence per week." He also constructed "an electrical machine, first with a glass phial, and afterwards with a real cylinder."

One day, as he was walking near Fleet Street, he noticed on a billboard the announcement of a series of lectures on natural philosophy to be delivered by Mr Tatum—price, one shilling per lecture. Faraday was anxious to attend these lectures, but he had neither the time nor the money for the purpose. Luck was on his side, however, for both his employer and his brother came to his aid. His employer generously allowed him to take time off from his work; and his brother Robert, with equal generosity, supplied him with the price of admission.

And thus he received another taste of science and took a further step toward his future career. But Faraday was as yet unaware of his destiny as one of the pioneer scientists of the world. He expected to remain all his life a bookbinder—a man only superficially connected with the world of thought. From his apprenticeship at Riebau's he graduated to the position of journeyman binder to M. de la Roche—a Frenchman who possessed neither the sympathy nor the intelligence of Mr Riebau. After a short and disagreeable trial Faraday left his employer and began to look for a job in another bindery.

It was a critical time for Michael. His father was now dead, and his mother was in direst poverty. And try as he would, he couldn't find another job as a bookbinder. What in the world was he to do?

This was one of the darkest hours of his life—and the fore-runner of one of his brightest days. For, as he was desperately trying to find his way through the night, the famous English scientist Sir Humphry Davy was making his greatest discovery—the discovery of Michael Faraday.

II

"TRY DESPERATELY to succeed—and do not hope for success." This was Faraday's motto throughout his life, and it was in accordance with this motto that he met Sir Humphry Davy. In the course of his apprenticeship he had attended some of Sir Humphry's lectures and had copied them out in a neat hand and given them an attractive binding. He now sent these notes to Sir Humphry—Michael was modest but he was not timid—and he respectfully asked the great scientist for a job in his laboratory. He expected no answer to this request, for he had received no answer to a similar request which he had made to another scientist—Sir Joseph Banks. But much to his surprise he got not only a reply but a job from Sir Humphry. Officially his new position was that of assistant to Sir Humphry in the laboratory of the Royal Institution. Actually his duties consisted in washing the bottles, polishing the desks, cleaning the inkwells and sweeping the floors of the laboratory. Faraday had been promoted from a bookbinder to a janitor.

But before long he was able to demonstrate to Sir Humphry that he was much more than a janitor. His quick mind, his analytical perception and his helpful though deferential suggestions established him as a fellow-wanderer "into regions yet untrod" and fellow-reader of "what is still unread in the manuscripts of God." Sir Humphry allowed him to take an active part in his experiments. In some of these experiments both Davy and Faraday sustained injuries, though fortunately of a minor nature. "Of these," writes Faraday to his friend Benjamin Abbot, "the most terrible was ... when a compound of chlorine and azote ... exploded ... The explosion was so rapid as to blow my hand open . . . and to tear off a part of one of my nails . . . Sir Humphry received several cuts on his hands and face ..."

And thus they worked side by side—master and servant, or rather teacher and pupil—exploring the mysteries of nature, interpreting its symbols and taming its powers. And more and more as they worked together, the teacher began to rely upon the pupil. Within a few months Sir Humphry was so thoroughly convinced of Faraday's ability that he invited him to accompany him as his "philosophical assistant" on a series of lectures throughout the leading cities of Europe.

To the blacksmith's young son (of twenty-two) who had never traveled beyond the horizon's distance from London this continental journey was nothing short of a miracle. He started on his journey on Wednesday, October 13, 1813. "This morning," he wrote in his diary, "forms an epoch in my life."

His journey proved to be full of surprises—some of them pleasant, others painful, all of them informative. In his diary he noted his excitement at the "luminescence of the sea at night," the solemn grandeur of the mountains, his first sight of a glow-worm, the forest of Fontainebleau "dressed in its airy garment of crystalline hoar frost," the crater of Vesuvius—"that bottomless gulf which belches forth wreaths of smoke and showers of flaming rocks." In Paris he caught a glimpse of Napoleon "sitting in one corner of his carriage, covered and almost hidden by an enormous robe of ermine, and his face overshadowed by a tremendous plume of feathers." He was delighted at the unexpected nobility of the human heart when he noted that the English scientists were allowed free passports in France although the English armies were fighting against the armies of France. And he was chagrined at the unexpected meanness of the human heart when he observed Lady Davy's attitude toward him. Although Faraday was now recognized everywhere as Davy's philosophical assistant, Lady Davy treated him as her husband's lackey. "She likes to show her authority," he wrote to Abbot, "and I find her extremely earnest in mortifying me." She took every opportunity to "show him his place," forgetting that her own husband had but recently risen from a similar place. Finally she reached the climax of her petty annoyances. It was at Geneva. The Genevese philosopher, Professor de la Rive, had invited Faraday as well as the Davys to dinner. A place had been set at the table for Faraday as a mark of his equality with the rest of the company. But Lady Davy objected. Faraday, she insisted, was her husband's servant and as such must be compelled to eat with the other servants.

Whereupon Professor de la Rive, to show his disgust for Lady Davy's conduct, ordered dinner to be served in a separate room for Faraday, as befitted the dignity of "a lonely young philosopher who lived above the petty squabbles of his fellows."

Faraday swallowed his humiliation with a wholesome seasoning of philosophy. This experience had provided him with the data for a new and interesting scientific observation. The human mind, he noted, is a peculiar compound of sublimity and slime.

III

IN THE SPRING OF 1815 Sir Humphry and his assistant started back for England. "You may be sure," Faraday wrote hurriedly to his mother, "that my first moments will be in your company . . ." And then he added a postscript: " 'Tis the shortest and (to me) the sweetest letter I ever wrote you."

He was delighted to return home and to resume his job as assistant technician at the laboratory of the Royal Institution. The Institution was a combined technical school, public lecture forum and learned society. Though but fifteen years old at the time of Faraday's return from the Continent, it had already come to be recognized as "the home of the highest kind of scientific research, and of the best and most specialized kind of scientific lectures." And now Faraday was accepted as an integral part of the organization—not only as a research student but as an occasional lecturer. One of his friends gives us a vivid if rather crude picture of the young scientist as he appeared on the platform:

> *Warmth in his heart, good humor in his face,*
> *A friend to mirth but foe to vile grimace—*
> *Neat was the youth in dress, in person plain,*
> *A mind that toiled for truth and not for gain.*

His earnings at this time were scanty—thirty shillings a week— but they were sufficient for his needs. Indeed, he considered them sufficient for the needs of two instead of one. For he began to pay court to a young lady—Sarah Barnard. Earlier in life, to be sure, he had written in his notebook a diatribe against love. "What is love? A nuisance to everybody but the parties concerned." But now he persisted in declaring his love even to the nuisance of his beloved. When he made her a written proposal of marriage she penned on the margin of the letter—"Love makes philosophers into fools."

But the philosopher persisted in his folly, and finally Miss Barnard consented—to the lifelong happiness of both. For the wife turned out to be a perfect complement to the husband. If Michael Faraday never cared for money, Sarah Faraday never cared for the luxuries that money could buy. For nearly half a century she took tender care of his body and left his mind free to travel in the poetical fairyland of scientific research.

And it was indeed a fairy world in which he lived—an impractical child seeking for adventure in an unexplored land of perpetual enchantment. His genius in the fields of chemistry and of electricity had amazed all England. His services as an expert were in constant demand in the law courts. For a short time he yielded to this demand and within a single year he earned for his expert testimony no less than $5,000. If he continued with this work, his friends advised him, he could confidently look forward to about $25,000 a year. But he gave it all up in order to be free to pursue his scientific investigations.

And it was about this time (1827) that he passed up another opportunity for worldly success. He had been offered the chair of chemistry at the University of London, but he declined the offer. His scientific researches at the Royal Institution required all his time and energy.

And the salary that he now received for "the variety of his duties"—we are quoting the memorandum of the directors of the Royal Institution—and for "the zeal and ability with which he performs these duties" was "£100 (about $500) per annum, house, coals, and candles." A poor enough return for the "most important discoveries of the day"—but it was all that the directors of the Royal Institution, with their inadequate endowment, were able to afford. "We are living on the parings of our own skin."

[*124*]

This, then, was the sacrifice of Faraday in the cause of science. And it was a sacrifice most cheerfully endured. For Faraday did not regard himself as a martyr. He enjoyed the simplicity of his life—with its zestful labors and its joyful discoveries. Whenever in the course of an experiment he found the key to a new truth, he leaped and shouted like a child. And, too, in his leisure moments he *played* like a child. He loved his recreation as he loved his work. Theaters, horse races, dances (he once went to a masked ball dressed in a nightgown and a nightcap), occasional trips to the country to attend a husking bee or a sheep-shearing festival—such were the amusements that relaxed him in his brief vacations from his scientific labors.

And thus we see him tripping through the laboratory of his life—an observant, playful, thoughtful little child of a man, well below the average in height, but tough of muscle and resolute of mind—brown hair parted in the middle and covered with a hat that had to be especially made for him because of the unusual length of his head from front to back—ringing voice, wide and generous mouth, eyes full of fun and heart full of laughter.

Of *honest* laughter. His honesty was his greatest glory—and his severest handicap. When his associates at the Institution asked him for his opinion about their work, he gave them his frank appraisal rather than his unreserved praise. And this frankness on his part gained him not a few enmities—including even that of the man whom he most greatly admired, Sir Humphry Davy. One of Sir Humphry's most important inventions was the "safety lamp"—a miners' lantern which, Sir Humphry claimed, would never explode. When Faraday examined this safety lamp, however, he found that it was not always safe. And he so reported to the Parliamentary Committee investigating the hazards of the British mines. The life of the miners, he felt, was more important than the honor of his teacher.

But Davy felt otherwise. He resented the "tittle-tattle" of his former "servant," and he questioned the competence of this "young upstart" to pass upon the work of his master. For several years he harbored this grudge against Faraday, and finally he got his revenge. A number of Faraday's admirers had proposed him as a candidate for the Fellowship of the Royal Society, a scientific body of which Sir Humphry was President. When Faraday's name came up for election, there was one black ball against him—that of Sir Humphry Davy.

This one negative vote was insufficient, of course, to hurt the reputation of Faraday. But it did much to sully the name of Davy. Yet Faraday bore no resentment against his former master and present adversary. "He never forgot," writes Jean Dumas in his *Eloge Historique,* "what he owed to Davy." Years afterwards, when Sir Humphry was dead, Faraday was chatting with Dumas in the library of the Royal Institution. Suddenly he pointed to Sir Humphry's picture and said in a voice trembling with emotion: "There, my friend, was a great man!"

IV

FARADAY had no time for petty bickerings or personal spites. For he had dedicated his entire life to a single task—the deciphering of the secret alphabet of nature. His purpose, he said, was not to build machines but merely to discover facts. "Let others attend to the harnessing of the forces of nature. I am content merely with the study of the correlation of these forces." For he was a philosopher as well as a scientist. He was anxious to find a unifying principle in the multitudinous diversity of nature. Again and again in his notebooks we come across such expressions as the following: *Try to convert magnetism into electricity ... Study affinities between gases and liquids ... Connection between magnetism and gravity ... Are all phases of electricity identical in nature? ... Correlation between electricity and light ...* Always seeking to discover the one divine answer to all our human riddles.

His extended career of discovery may be roughly divided into three periods:

In the first period (1816–1830) he experimented largely in the field of chemistry, with occasional excursions into the mysteries of magnetism. He studied the composition of glass, the nature of boracic acid, the separation of manganese from iron and the production—for scientific study rather than for practical use—of rustless steel. But more and more his interests were drawn to the problems of "electro-magnetic rotation." The law of magnetic revolution, he wrote to Professor de la Rive, "is simple and beautiful." The orbit of an electric wire around a magnetic pole and the orbit of the earth around the sun—were they not perhaps the interwoven threads of a simple and harmonious design of nature?

In order to explore the hidden harmonies of this possible design, the philosopher-scientist entered upon the second period of his investigation (1831–1839). In this period he devoted himself almost exclusively to magnetism and electricity. "I am busy just now on electro-magnetism," he wrote to his friend, Richard Phillips, "and think I have got hold of a good thing, but can't say. It may be a weed instead of a fish that after all my labor I may at last pull up." And, indeed, time and again he pulled up "a weed instead of a fish." His notebooks are full of the constantly reiterated expression—"No result."

One day as he was working in his laboratory, however, he suddenly cried to his assistant, "Do you see, do you see?" He had succeeded at last in converting magnetism into electricity. To Faraday it was but another manifestation of the unity of nature. To the rest of the world this discovery marked the beginning of the age of electrical machines.

But Faraday paid a high toll for this discovery. "I am so involved in my experiments," he had written to Professor de la Rive, "that I have hardly time for my meals." As a result of this strain his health had become undermined until finally his doctor ordered him to take a protracted vacation. It was not until five years later that he was able to enter upon the third period of his investigations (1844–1860). In this period he ranged over a wide field of miscellaneous experiments, the most important of them dealing with the relationship between electricity and light. It was from the inspired mind of Faraday that Edison first received the electric spark which today illumines the world.

V

AT THE CONCLUSION of his daily work Faraday was accustomed to watch the sunset hand in hand with his wife. "A glorious sunset," he wrote to one of his friends, "brings with it a thousand thoughts that delight me." To the end of his life he enjoyed looking at the day as it folded up into the chrysalis of the night— only to rise into the wings of another day. "How old and how beautiful is this figure of the resurrection!" he remarked in his journal.

His strength, overtaxed by his laborious experiments, was failing again. Together with his waning strength be began to notice a gradual failing of his memory. With his customary gentle humor he refers to this infirmity in one of his letters to his friend, Professor Schönbein: "I have no doubt my answer to your letter is very unsatisfactory. But, my dear friend, please *remember* that I *forget,* and that I can no more help it than a sieve can help the water running out of it."

And it was with his customary gentle humor that he watched the ebbing away of his own life. "The important thing," he said, "is to know how to take all things quietly."

One day an employee of the Royal Mint, a young man by the name of Joseph Newton, was sent down to perform an experiment at the laboratory of the Royal Institution. He noticed an old man, dressed in a shabby suit, observing him with a whimsical look in his eye. "I suppose," said Newton, "you've been here for a number of years?"

"Yes, a good many years."

"Sort of janitor here?"

"Yes, sort of."

"I hope they pay you well?"

"I *could* stand a little better pay."

"And what, my man, is your name?"

"Michael Faraday."

Plain Michael Faraday to the last.

DARWIN

Great Scientific Contributions by Darwin

Formulated the theory of evolution.

BOOKS AND TREATISES:
The Voyage of the Beagle.
The Origin of Species.
The Descent of Man.
The Variation of Animals and Plants.
The Expression of the Emotions.
Volcanic Islands.
Fertilization of Orchids.
Movement in Plants.
Geological Observations.

Darwin

Charles Robert Darwin

1809–1882

PASCAL ONCE REMARKED that the entire face of the world was changed by the shape of Cleopatra's nose. Almost two thousand years later the entire face of history was nearly changed by the shape of another nose. In the fall of 1831 the twenty-two-year-old divinity student, Charles Darwin, was about to sail as an unpaid naturalist on His Majesty's ship, the *Beagle*. But Captain Fitzroy, who commanded the *Beagle,* hesitated to take Darwin along because he judged, from the shape of Darwin's nose, that the young man had "neither the mentality nor the energy" to become a good scientist.

Had Darwin never sailed on the *Beagle,* he would most likely have taken Holy Orders and science would have lost one of its epoch-making works—the story of the evolution of the human race. Fortunately for the advancement of learning, however, Captain Fitzroy changed his mind about the shape of Darwin's nose and Darwin was allowed to sail on the *Beagle*. And thus the young theological student was launched upon a religious adventure of a new kind. He set out to explore and to interpret the word of God as inscribed in the Bible of Living Things. From the classroom of theology, the study of God, he graduated into the priesthood of anthropology, the study of Man. And it was the lifelong devotion of his priesthood to acquaint his fellow men with the story of their epic though as yet far from completed journey from the lowly to the sublime.

II

DARWIN was born at Shrewsbury, on the same day with Abraham Lincoln (February 12, 1809)—a coincidence which led one of his biographers to see him as "the emancipator of the human mind from the shackles of ignorance, just as Lincoln was the emancipator of the human body from the shackles of slavery." The year 1809 was lavish with its meteoric shower of geniuses. In that one year an entire basketful of them was dropped into the lap of humanity—Darwin, Lincoln, Gladstone, Chopin, Mendelssohn, Poe, Tennyson, Oliver Wendell Holmes and Elizabeth Barrett Browning, to mention only a few. Every one of these "superior children of the human race" contributed something toward the permanent beauty and nobility of the world— and the contribution of Darwin was not the least among them.

He came of excellent stock on both sides. His paternal grandfather, Erasmus Darwin, was a famous naturalist who wrote a poem on the *Loves of the Plants* and a prose work on the *Laws of Organic Life*. His great-grandfather on his mother's side was Josiah Wedgwood, the celebrated founder of the Wedgwood potteries. A healthy interest in the arts and sciences, therefore, was only to be expected in the Darwin household.

As a child Darwin was gentle, meditative and acutely observant of his surroundings. Even when he was confronted with danger he was able to pursue his observations in the midst of his fear. One day, absorbed as usual in his thoughts, he was walking through the fortifications of Shrewsbury and stepped absent-mindedly over a parapet. Suddenly he found himself falling through the air—to his death, as he believed. Yet his wits were alert. This was but another interesting experiment for a scientifically-minded little fellow. "The number of thoughts which passed through my head during this very short but sudden and wholly unexpected fall was astonishing . . . all of which seemed hardly compatible with what physiologists have . . . stated about each thought requiring an appreciable amount of time."

From his earliest childhood he formed the habit of noticing things for himself. He loved to collect and to study all sorts of pebbles, shells, coins, birds' eggs, flowers and insects. He rarely captured his insects alive, preferring to pick them up when he found them dead. For he didn't think it right to kill them with his own hands. Yet with the naive logic of childhood he felt no compunction about killing birds with a gun—at a distance. He enjoyed hunting for a number of years, until one day he saw the struggles of a wounded bird and made up his mind not ever again to bring suffering or death to any living creature for the mere sake of sport. "A gentle heart," said an ancient philosopher, "is but another name for a vivid imagination."

Darwin inherited his gentleness from his mother. But he had little opportunity to know her well, for she died when he was eight years old. His father, Doctor Robert Waring Darwin, was a huge mountain of joviality and efficiency—he weighed something like three hundred and fifty pounds—and, in the words of his son, "one of the wisest of men." Yet he was not sufficiently wise to understand his son's character. He considered Charles a good-for-nothing loafer whose only mission in life was to "mess up the house with his everlasting rubbish." In order to knock some "old-fashioned common sense" into his head, Doctor Darwin sent Charles to a classical school. But the youngster paid no attention to his Latin and his Greek. Instead, he fixed up a secret laboratory in his father's garden and began to dabble in chemistry and in physics. This, in the opinion both of his schoolmates and of his teachers, was "the activity of a deranged mind." The boys nicknamed him "Gas"; the head master gave him up as a *poco curante*—a rather careless creature; and his father, disgusted with his experimenting and his "rat-catching," removed him from the classical school and sent him up to Edinburgh University to study medicine.

At first Darwin was not disinclined to follow in his father's footsteps. But the lectures on anatomy soon began to bore him. And as for the lectures on materia medica, he found them "something fearful to listen to." Moreover, his sympathetic temperament couldn't bear the sight of the surgical demonstrations. One day, as an operation was being performed on a child, he rushed out of the amphitheater. At that period they were still operating without anaesthesia, and the screams of the agonized child kept haunting him for years.

It was quite evident to Darwin's father that his son was not cut out to be a doctor. And so he tried to turn him into a clergyman. As a youngster Charles had shown distinct religious tendencies. As he ran to school each morning after breakfast he prayed to the Lord to aid him in arriving before it was too late. But—and this was a point which his father had overlooked—Darwin started so late for school that it was *necessary* to pray. The youngster was not the type to adapt himself to the conventional life of the student. For three years he drifted lazily along the curricular requirements of Christ's College, Cambridge—years that were "sadly wasted," as he tells us, "in praying, drinking, singing, flirting and card-playing."

Yet it was here that he met the eminent scientist, Professor Henslow, through whose recommendation he was allowed to sail as a naturalist on the *Beagle*. Fortunately Doctor Darwin was wealthy enough to indulge his son in his "impractical whims." The hurdle of financial worry, at least, would be removed from his "unprofitable" quest for scientific truth.

III

FOR FIVE YEARS (1831–1836) the *Beagle* sailed over the seas and Darwin was privileged to behold with his own eyes "the rondure of the world and the mysteries of its teeming life." With the precision of a scientist and the imagination of a poet—for every great scientist *is* a poet—he collected, observed and classified the scattered fragments of the Chinese puzzle of existence and tried to piece them together into a comprehensive and comprehensible design.

Thus far, however, he had formed no definite idea as to the direction in which his investigations were leading him. Like every true observer, he started not with a theory but with facts. It was to take him twenty years of laborious research before he could determine that his vast accumulation of facts, when examined impartially, pointed to but a single theory—the theory of evolution.

The whole world to Darwin was a big question mark—a problem in mathematics with many unknown quantities, a geometric theorem which must be solved rather than a work of art which must be admired. He confessed that at a very early age he had lost his taste for literature, art and music. But he had found the other side of the golden coins of literature and art and music in his science.

And he possessed one precious thing that was greater even than his passion for science—and that was, a love for his fellow men. Once, when the *Beagle* had anchored off the coast of Brazil, he saw an old Negro woman, in a party of runaway slaves, dash herself to death over a precipice in order to escape from her pursuers. "In a Roman matron," he observed, "this would have been called the noble love of freedom. In a poor Negress it is regarded as mere brutal obstinacy."

The barbarism of slavery disgusted and repelled him beyond measure. "Near Rio de Janeiro," he records in his *Beagle Journal*, "I lived opposite to an old lady who kept screws to crush the fingers of her female slaves. I have stayed in a house where a young mulatto, daily and hourly, was reviled, beaten and persecuted enough to break the spirit of the lowest animal." Twenty years before the Civil War he expressed his detestation of slavery in words as passionate as ever came from the lips of an American abolitionist. "Those who look tenderly at the slave owner and with a cold heart at the slave, never seem to put themselves into the position of the latter ... What a cheerless prospect, with not even a hope of change! Picture to yourself the chance, ever hanging over you, of your wife and your little children—those objects which nature urges even the slave to call his own—being torn from you and sold like beasts to the first bidder! And these deeds"—here speaks the spirit of William Lloyd Garrison himself—"these deeds are done and palliated by men who profess to love their neighbors as themselves, who believe in God, and pray that His Will be done on earth!"

Throughout his life Darwin kept his heart open to the sufferings of men just as he kept his eye open to the secret of their descent.

And his sensitive heart and observant eye were lodged in a feeble frame. Darwin inherited his father's stature, but he did not inherit his father's strength. His trip on the *Beagle* was an unmitigated torture of protracted sea-sickness. Added to the sufferings of ill health were the discomforts of a voyage that were enough to undermine the constitution of a more powerful man than Darwin. The food was insufficient and indigestible—to the end of his days Darwin suffered from repeated attacks of vomiting as a result of the "poisons he had absorbed on the *Beagle*." There were frequent spells of unendurable cold and unendurable heat. Again and again, in the swampy regions that he visited in his search for scientific data, he suffered from the bites of venomous insects. On some of his explorations into the jungle he was obliged to go for days at a time without water. Undermined by the accumulation of these hardships he returned from his voyage a broken man.

But a man eager for the adventure of science—and for the no less exacting adventure of marriage. Shortly after his return from his voyage he married his cousin, Emma Wedgwood, bought a large country house with a spacious garden, and settled down to raise a family of ten children and to discover if possible "the secret of their true ancestry."

As a first step in his search for the ancestry of the human race he compiled the story of his discoveries during his voyage on the *Beagle*—a scientific treatise that reads like a fascinating romance. For in everything that he wrote he had but a single aim—to make clear to others the truth as it appeared to him. "Honest simplicity" was his lifelong motto. "It is a golden rule," he said, "always to use, if possible, a short old Saxon word. Such a sentence as 'so purely dependent is the incipient plant on the specific morphological tendency' does not sound to my ears like good mother English—it wants translating . . . I think too much pains cannot be taken in making the style transparently clear and throwing eloquence to the dogs."

And he did have to take great pains in order to make his style transparently clear. He found good composition extremely difficult, and it was only by dogged determination that he was able to hammer out a free and easy and interesting style. "It's dogged as does it," he wrote upon a card which he pinned up over his desk.

He regretted that he had no taste for poetry, and yet his *Voyage of the Beagle* is full of poetical passages. Note, for example, his description of Brazil: "The land is one great, wild, untidy, luxuriant hothouse, made by Nature for herself, but taken possession of by man, who has studded it with gay houses and formal gardens." The first sight of this country threw him into "a perfect hurricane of delight and astonishment . . . The form of the orange-tree, the cocoanut, the palm, the mango, the tree-fern, the banana, will remain clear and separate; but the thousand beauties which united these into one perfect scene must fade away. Yet they will leave, like a tale heard in childhood, a picture full of indistinct but most beautiful figures."

The *Voyage of the Beagle,* after a hundred years, is still as romantic as a tale of adventure out of the Arabian Nights.

Darwin's next book, however, was more purely scientific. It dealt with the nature and the habits of the barnacle, that curious little sea-animal which "stands on its head in the bottom of its shell-cup and kicks its food into its mouth with its feet." It took Darwin eight years to write this book. And they were perhaps the busiest eight years of his life. In sticking to this one subject for so long a period, Darwin seemed to have absorbed into his own character something of the tenacity of the barnacle. A good many of his friends ridiculed him for wasting so much good effort on so unprofitable a task. But he was winning a reputation as an outstanding naturalist and he was training the sinews of his intellect for the great work of his life.

For throughout these years he was gradually gathering his material, sifting it carefully through his critical mind, and building up his theory about the Origin of Species and the Ascent (misnamed the Descent) of Man.

IV

THE THEORY OF EVOLUTION was not original with Darwin. Thousands of years before the Christian era the writers of the Chinese sagas had expressed a vague idea of the development of man from the lower animals. This idea had received further elaboration at the hands of the Greek philosopher, Epicurus (342–270 B.C.), and of the Roman poet, Lucretius (96–55 B.C.). With the coming of Christianity, however, the story of Creation had superseded the theory of evolution, and it was not until Darwin's day that this theory was resurrected and placed upon a scientific basis.

When Darwin was ready to publish his theory of evolution he felt, as he put it, "like a prospective murderer." For he was about to kill the orthodox ideas about man and God. He expected everybody to treat him with contempt. In a letter to his friend, Professor Asa Gray of Harvard University, he wrote: "As an honest man, I must tell you that I have come to the heterodox conclusion that there are no such things as independently created species ... I know this will make you despise me ..."

But his genius had enabled him to come upon a great discovery, and his honesty would not let him rest until he made this discovery known to the world. And so he felt it his duty to kill an old dogma in order to reëstablish what he regarded as a still older truth.

But if he had to kill, he did so with a gentle thrust. At no point did he descend to bitter controversy. He simply stated his own side without attacking the other side. Indeed, he stated no side whatsoever—he merely presented facts. He did not want to hurt anybody or to disturb anybody's belief. "Let each man hope and believe as he can." As for himself, he found it not only reasonable but comforting to believe that man had risen from savagery to civilization rather than that he had fallen from civilization to savagery. His theory of evolution gave him the groundwork for a New Testament of his own—the Bible of the progress of man.

He had first formulated this theory of progress, in a tentative outline, as early as 1839—twenty years before the publication of the *Origin of Species*. In 1842 he developed this outline into a sketch of 35 pages, and in 1844 he expanded it further into a manuscript of 230 pages. But instead of printing this manuscript he continued for another fifteen years to test his data, to pick flaws in his arguments, and to check and recheck his conclusions over and over again. For he was, throughout his career, his own most exacting critic, with the result that he was able to anticipate and to answer practically all the objections that were later to be raised by his opponents.

It was not until 1858 that Darwin was ready at last to publish the result of his investigations. And then, just as he was putting the finishing touches to his manuscript, he awoke one day to find that another scientist had unwittingly stolen all his thunder. On June the 18th of that year he received from his friend, Alfred

Russel Wallace, an original paper on Evolution with a request for his frank criticism as to the validity of the theory. Wallace was at that time living on the other side of the globe (in Malaya). He was altogether unaware of the fact that Darwin, too, had hit upon the idea of the origin of species and that he had been quietly working on this idea for the past twenty years. And so it was with the utmost innocence that he was now asking Darwin to introduce *him* to the world as the originator of the evolutionary theory.

What was Darwin to do in this predicament? Wallace's article was an exact transcript of his own findings on the subject. "I never saw a more striking coincidence!" exclaimed Darwin in a letter to the famous geologist, Doctor Lyell. "If Wallace had had my manuscript sketch written out in 1842, he could not have made a better short abstract."

Darwin's first impulse was to step aside and to give Wallace the entire credit for the discovery. "I would far rather burn my whole book," he said, "than that he or any other man should think that I had behaved in a paltry spirit." Doctor Lyell, however, insisted that in all fairness to himself Darwin ought to publish his own views at once. He expressed his conviction that Wallace would gladly accept the situation as soon as he learned that Darwin had anticipated him in the discovery by about twenty years.

Finally Darwin agreed to have the theory presented to the Linnaean Society as the *joint* work of Wallace and himself. And Wallace, not to be outdone in generosity, declared it to be "a singular piece of good luck" that gave him any share in "a discovery for which Darwin alone was responsible."

And thus ended one of the most remarkable controversies in history—a controversy in which each of the opponents tried to advance the interests of the other at the expense of his own glory.

Now that the theory had been presented to the scientific world, Darwin went rapidly ahead with the preparation of his manuscript for the general public. The first edition of the book was issued on November 24, 1859, under the cumbersome title— *The Origin of Species by Means of Natural Selection or the Preservation of Favored Races in the Struggle for Life.*

This book, which "swept away the story of Adam and Eve and the Garden of Eden in a deluge of scientific data," may be briefly summarized as follows: In this world of ours there is constantly being produced an unlimited multiplication of living creatures. The food supply, however, is limited. So, too, is the available living-space in the world. The result is a life-and-death competition between all living things, an everlasting struggle for existence. Those that are best fitted to their environment are able to live, and the rest are doomed to die. The evolutionists call this process the "survival of the fittest." But in the course of time the environment keeps changing—from sea to land, from valleys to mountains, from glacial periods to periods of warmer climate, and so on. During these changes it becomes necessary for the living creatures also to change, or to *evolve* from one species to another, in order that they may survive under the new conditions. The process by which this *evolution* takes place is called *natural selection*—that is, nature's selection of those characteristics which enable the species to survive, and her elimination of those characteristics which are no longer necessary for survival in the new environment.

This, in a nutshell, is the whole story of evolution. The unlimited multiplication of life leads to a struggle for existence and to the survival of the fittest through the process of natural selection and the consequent development from one species to another. In accordance with this theory, man is but a step removed from the so-called lower animals. Darwin explains this step in his next book—*The Descent of Man.*

Darwin is generally credited (or discredited) with the theory that men are descended from monkeys. As a matter of fact, he never said anything of the sort. He believed that men and apes are both evolved from a common prehistoric ancestor that is now extinct. The ape, in other words, is not our forefather but our distant cousin.

Man, according to Darwin, is the highest form of animal life on earth. He has gained the mastery over the other animals through the law of the survival of the fittest. By the word *fittest* Darwin means not necessarily the strongest or the most ruthless but the *most adaptable*. Among the lower animals, to be sure, natural selection assumes the form of elimination through physical strife. Within the human sphere, however, the process of individual strife is being gradually superseded by the progress of social coöperation. Selfish aggressiveness is giving way to mutual aid. In spite of our occasional lapses—such as the ephemeral triumphs of a Napoleon or a Hitler—the law of civilization is slowly but surely emerging out of the lawlessness of the jungle. Step by step we are absorbing the lesson that the best way to insure the survival of the individual human being is to work for the friendly collaboration of the entire human race.

Man, believes Darwin, is a social animal. He is not a fallen angel, but a risen savage. His path is not downward, but upward. Yet, on the other hand, he is not a creature set apart from all other living creatures. On the contrary, he is intimately related to everything that moves and breathes and struggles to live. In the scale of evolving life he is still to be classed as an animal. But he is an animal with an infinite capacity for love.

V

THE LIFE OF DARWIN was perhaps the best proof of his theory of evolution. His capacity for love seemed to grow from year to year. He was drawn to people, and people in turn were drawn to him. In his bluish-gray eyes there was a perpetual twinkle of sympathetic understanding. Such was the kindly serenity of his face that strangers would come away from their first visit with tears of joy in their eyes. As for his intimate friends—and he had many of them—they found in his gentle personality a "perpetual benediction." For friendship to Darwin was the greatest of all the blessings bestowed upon the human race. "Talk of fame, honor, pleasure, wealth," he wrote in one of his letters, "all these are dirt compared with the affection of friendship."

But the friendliness of his character was most apparent in his attitude toward his enemies. In spite of all their vituperations, he never uttered a harsh word against any of them. On the contrary, he always thanked them for their criticism. For the primary object of his life, he said, was to ascertain the truth. And in the search of the hidden byways of truth, "two minds are better than one." He was at all times ready to acknowledge the weak links in the chain of his arguments—to concede his defeat whenever the arguments of his opponents were more convincing than his own. "If I am wrong, the sooner I am knocked on the head and annihilated so much the better."

He never assumed a superior attitude either toward his antagonists or toward his collaborators. Throughout his life he acted the part of the humble assistant rather than that of the imposing master. He was especially grateful to the unrecognized workers in the laboratory, the uninspired gatherers of data, the "hodmen of science," for the invaluable help they were able to give him. He looked down upon no creature, however lowly. His servants, like the members of his family, were in his eyes invested with the selfsame dignity—the dignity of their common membership in the society of the human race.

He possessed that true stamp of the superior mind—a modest honesty. One day Gladstone paid him a visit. When the Prime Minister left him, Darwin remarked: "Mr Gladstone seemed to be quite unaware that he was a great man, and talked to me as if he were an ordinary person like myself." To which remark Gladstone, when it was reported to him, replied: "My feeling toward Mr Darwin was exactly the same as Mr Darwin's feeling toward me."

Darwin had something of Buddha's fellow feeling toward all mankind—indeed, toward all nature. He talked about trees and grass as if they were living things. He would scold a plant-leaf for its "ingenuity" in screwing itself out of a basin of water in which he had tried to immerse it. Vexed with the behavior of certain seedlings with which he was experimenting, he said: "The little beggars are doing just what I don't want them to." He looked upon every plant as upon a living personality. He enjoyed the beauty of his flowers, and he was thankful to them for the "graciousness" of their beauty. He would touch their petals gently, with the infinite love of a sage and the simple admiration of a child.

His character was Christlike, yet he refused to call himself a Christian. "For myself," he said, "I do not believe that there ever has been any revelation." He was not, however, an atheist, but regarded himself rather as an agnostic. He was not very certain, he said, of his belief in God. But he was quite certain of his belief in man. "I believe that in the distant future man will be a far more perfect creature than he is today." As for the immortal destiny of the individual soul, on this question too he was an agnostic. "The whole subject (of immortality)," he said, "is beyond the scope of man's intellect . . . But man can do his duty."

His own duty, as he saw it, was to toil unflinchingly throughout his life in order to bring a little more light to his fellow men. And he toiled, as we have seen, under two tremendous handicaps —his wealth, which made hard labor unnecessary, and his suffering, which made any kind of labor almost impossible. But he overcame his handicaps, thanks to his own firmness and to the gentleness of his wife. For Emma Darwin, whom he immortalized as "the best and kindest of wives," was the "one condition which enabled him to bear the strain and fight out the struggle to the end." Passionately devoted though she was to the doctrines of the English Church, she nevertheless stood side by side with her agnostic husband. She attuned her life to the slower tempo of his own semi-invalid existence, she encouraged him without ever driving him, she kept in touch with his experiments, she corrected his proofs and she fortified his arguments with effective words and phrases. Above all, whenever he was in pain she cared for him with such uncomplaining tenderness that he often said to her: "It is almost worth while to be sick to be nursed by you."

But Darwin repaid his wife's devotion with an equally tender devotion of his own. And the beautiful harmony of their life was reflected in the characters of their children. The Darwins were a family of *thoroughbreds*—all of them were thoroughly bred in the best British tradition of joyousness, generosity and mutual respect.

The sense of respect—that is, the habit of sympathetic thoughtfulness for the feelings of others—was the keynote of the Darwin character. On his last visit to London, at the age of 73, Darwin was seized with a fainting spell just as he was about to enter the house of a friend. The friend was out; but the butler, noticing Darwin's condition, urged him to come inside.

"Please don't trouble yourself. I shall find a cab to take me home." And the considerate old naturalist staggered away from the door.

For three months he waited patiently for the end. "I am not the least afraid to die," he said. "I am only sorry that I haven't the strength to go on with my research."

His death was the signal for a worldwide chorus of denunciation. His enemies consigned his "unrepentant soul" to hell. But one old lady in England thought otherwise. "To be sure Darwin has proved there is no God," she said. "But God is so kind He will forgive him."

HUXLEY

Great Scientific Contributions by Huxley

BOOKS:
On the Anatomy of Medusae.
The Theory of the Vertebrate
    Skull.
Physiography.
Man's Place in Nature.
Essays on various scientific sub-
    jects.

Lay Sermons.
The Advance of Science.
The Crayfish.
Discourses Biological and Geo-
    logical.
Earthquakes and Volcanoes.
Evolution and Ethics.

Huxley

Thomas Henry Huxley

1825–1895

Physically I am the son of my mother. . . . I can hardly find any trace of my father in myself, except an inborn faculty for drawing . . . a hot temper . . . and that amount of tenacity of purpose which unfriendly observers sometimes call obstinacy."

He needed his obstinacy. He was a self-made man. Born at Ealing, just west of London, he entered the semi-public school of the district at eight, left it at ten, and never had another bit of regular schooling. His formal introduction to learning had left nothing but bitter memories. "The society I fell into at school was the worst I had ever known . . . The people who were set over us cared as much for our intellectual and moral welfare as if they were baby farmers." It was here that he received his first inkling of the struggle for existence. "Bullying was the least of the ill practices among us." Only the fittest survived.

Tom's father had been senior master of the Ealing School. But when the enterprise encountered financial difficulties, he was relieved of his post. Taking his family to Coventry he secured a position in a local savings bank. Troubled by his material worries he allowed Tom's mental faculties to "just naturally grow" without benefit of classes. As a result, young Huxley's educational curriculum consisted largely of a single R—Reading. Every morning before dawn he lit his candle, pinned a blanket around his shoulders, and sat up in his bed devouring all sorts of books on every conceivable subject. He had a picturesque mind. He could find an essay on geology as exciting as a novel, and a treatise on logic as invigorating as a drama.

It was in this informal manner that Huxley traveled over the endless road to knowledge. But he never drove himself unduly. "I worked extremely hard when it pleased me, and when it did not—which was a very frequent case—I was extremely idle."

His earliest desire, in spite of his mathematical deficiency, was to become a civil engineer. The idea of building bridges held a great fascination for him. But as he grew older he transferred his interests from the building of bridges to the healing of bodies. The entire Huxley family had gone "medicine minded." His sisters had become engaged to physicians and his brother, too, had started to explore "the deserts of anatomy" in order to discover the pathways to the oasis of health. Not to be outdone, Tom Huxley joined the family caravan.

For two years he studied medicine and then he hired himself out as an "assistant practitioner" to Dr Chandler—an acquaintance of the Huxleys who worked among the poor in the East End of London. Here Tom was able at first hand to observe the suffering that comes from poverty. "Alleys nine or ten feet wide . . . with tall houses full of squalid, drunken men and women, and the pavement littered with still more squalid children." Humanity reduced to the level of brutes—and treated as such. Huxley learned something else besides medicine in his ministrations among the poor. The world needed healing not only from its physical disease, but from its social sickness as well.

II

HE HAD RECEIVED a free scholarship at the Charing Cross Hospital, and he had taken honors in anatomy and physiology. He tried to enter the College of Surgeons but he was too young—not quite twenty. He was faced with several years of aimless drifting —a prospect he didn't like in the least—when events took a strange turn. One day a fellow student suggested that he join the navy. His vivid imagination took fire at the thought. He wrote a hasty letter to "influential" relatives, negotiated briskly, and reported for duty as assistant surgeon in the Haslar Naval Hospital.

Huxley was bored, however, with his new adventure as a sailor without a ship. He had hoped to be taken along on an expedition to the distant seas. And—such was the smiling temper of his fortune—his hope was realized. One day his superior, Sir John Richard, called him into his study. "Young man, how would you like to sail to the South Seas under Captain Stanley?"

Huxley's heart beat high. Stanley had taken part in a fabulous expedition to the Strait of Magellan and to the Arctic regions where he had almost lost his life. He was like a hero out of the old sagas. To sail with Captain Stanley! True enough, Huxley was to serve merely as a "half-officer" on the voyage. When he entered his tiny cabin on the *Rattlesnake*—Captain Stanley's ship—he was compelled to stoop in order to move about. But this cabin was a palace to the boy of twenty-one. Here he could dream to his heart's content—reading his books, studying through the microscope whatever strange specimens of life they might discover on the expedition, making sketches, taking notes, piercing incessantly through the sea-mists to new visions, new islands, new facts. Always he had an insatiable thirst for facts.

Huxley was not disappointed with his voyage. For in the course of it he found many an adventure. He charted mountain ranges that had never before been recorded; he helped to save a shipwrecked white woman who had been captured by natives; he struck up a friendship with a chieftain who claimed him as the spirit of his dead brother; he went ashore at Sydney and "danced the light fantastic" with the "elegant Australian girls." And—most exciting adventure of them all—he found himself "a ladylove exceeding fair with soft blue eyes and yellow hair." He wrote to his mother from Sydney and told her of his engagement. "Henrietta has been to school two years in Germany, speaks German, and is interested in German literature." Apparently these accomplishments would "put her right" in the eyes of a fond mother whose husband had once taught school.

But they decided not to marry until Huxley got established as a recognized scientist. He left Henrietta in Sydney and returned home to his influential friends. They suggested that he "go down to the meeting of the British Association and make himself notorious somehow or other." In order to succeed, they told him, a man must do "a little trumpeting now and then." Tom was a sensitive fellow, but love had taken complete sovereignty over him. With a feigned assurance that concealed a trembling heart he delivered a lecture on oceanic hydrozoa (underwater animals) before an audience of scholars who had a habit of "waving and wagging one coat-tail when they applauded." There appeared a small notice of this lecture in the *Literary Gazette*.

And then fortune smiled upon him again. He submitted for publication a paper he had written aboard the *Rattlesnake* on the anatomy of a species of jelly fish he had studied on his voyage. The paper was hailed as the basis for "a new branch of philosophic zoölogy." It was also the basis for Huxley's future success. It brought him the Royal Medal and an election to the Royal Society. "And now," he wrote enthusiastically to Henrietta, "if only I had four hundred pounds a year!"

And Henrietta wrote back—"Let us be patient."

III

THEY WERE MARRIED after seven years of patient waiting. Huxley was now one of the most promising young scientists in England. He had passed the goal of four hundred pounds a year. He was a contributor to the *Westminster Review,* a teacher at the Government School of Mines and a lecturer at the Royal

Institution. He faced his future prospects with "complete equanimity."

He especially enjoyed his teaching. The Government School of Mines had instituted free evening courses for workingmen. "Mass Education" had become the battle cry of the British intelligentsia. Everywhere in London the air was "pink with the new social philosophy." Huxley was an ideal teacher, a self-made man speaking in brisk unacademic language to self-made men. "I am sick of the dilettante middle class. I am glad I am not at Oxford. Here in London the air is free of the dons and the undergraduates and the ancient rituals." Here were workers who lived among *facts*. Huxley's explanations of the glacial epoch were masterpieces of melodrama. His style was racy. Thousands of people from every grade of society stormed the doors of the lecture hall. But only the laborers were admitted. All kinds of subterfuges were resorted to. One clerk attempted to gain admittance by asserting he was a "driver"—neglecting to add, however, that the only thing he "drove" was a quill.

It was at the School of Mines that Huxley at last found his vocation. He was to become a popularizer of science. With the magic wand of his intellect he touched the dead bones of antiquity—and behold, the bones took on flesh and came back to life.

Huxley was not only a popularizer of scientific knowledge, but a crusader for scientific causes. Any unrecognized pioneers? Huxley saw to it that they won recognition. Any challengers to a reasonable theory? Huxley was ready with a two-fisted intellect to enter the fight.

At this moment there was an unusually spirited fight raging around the new Darwinian theory of evolution. It offended the dignity of many people to acknowledge their descent from the lower animals. At a meeting of the British Association (in 1860) the Bishop of Oxford had turned to Thomas Huxley with a sarcastic smile. "I beg to know, is it through your grandfather or your grandmother that you claim your descent from a monkey?"

The audience was aghast. Tom Huxley's eyes glistened as he rose to his feet. He felt no need to be ashamed of having an ape for a grandfather, he asserted. "If there were an ancestor I might possibly feel shame in recalling it would be—a man like the Bishop of Oxford."

For twenty-five years the battle for evolution went on with unabated fury. And Huxley stayed always in the forefront of the fight. The newspapers headlined the issue, "Children of Adam, or Heirs of the Apes?" One of the contributors to *Punch* expressed himself on the subject in a little poem which a contemporary wag called *A Bit of Doggorilla:*

> *Am I satyr or man?*
> *Pray tell me who can,*
> *And settle my place in the scale.*
> *A man in ape's shape,*
> *An anthropoid ape,*
> *Or a monkey deprived of his tail?*

All England was divided on "the controversy of evolution which threatened to become a revolution." Huxley delivered scores of lectures in favor of Darwin. And these lectures kept constantly winning "new converts to irreligion." People who came to stone Huxley remained to applaud. His appeal was simple and eloquent. "Does my belief really brutalize and degrade mankind? Is the poet or the philosopher or the artist whose genius is the glory of his age degraded by the . . . certainty that he is the direct descendant of some naked and bestial savage whose intelligence was just sufficient to make him a little more cunning than the fox? . . . Or is he bound to howl and grovel on all fours because . . . he was once an egg?"

He collected his arguments and published them in a volume— *Man's Place in Nature*—which served as a challenging supplement to Darwin's *Origin of Species.* Darwin himself was a shy recluse who had no taste for public disputes. He had written a book on the abstruse physiological theory of the transmutation of species—a scientific treatise for which he expected nothing more exciting than a dignified burial in the dust of a paleontological library along with the other honored and innocuous dead. He was struck with amazement and alarm at the furor he had created. And then along came a faithful bulldog of a friend to protect him against the rage of his adversaries. He was relieved to find a man who not only understood him but who was ready to fight for him.

For Darwin himself was no fighter. He had never meant to set himself up as an iconoclast. He had been too deeply absorbed in the recreations of his insects to hear the rumblings of the thunder that he had set loose with his new ideas. And now that the storm had broken in all its fury he was content to pass on and to leave the field to those who had more heart for the fight.

IV

In all his quarrels Huxley had worthy associates. He belonged to the X Club—a coterie of "gentlemen assassins of other people's prejudices." They met once a month. On the day before the meeting the secretary sent to each member a simple reminder on a postcard—X, plus the date of the meeting. Once every summer there was a week-end picnic to which the members were asked to invite their ladies. The postcard for this event read— "X's + Y'vs." Although the gatherings were strictly informal, "just a few friends who did not want to drift apart," they nevertheless resulted in a whole "galaxy" of distinctions. Five of the members received the Royal Medal, three the Copley, one the Rumford. Six were presidents of the British Association; and three, presidents of the Royal Society.

It was at a meeting of the X Club that Huxley coined the word which defined his attitude toward religion. "In this club," one of the members had remarked, "most of us are atheists. We know there is no God." Whereupon Huxley retorted: "As for myself, I am merely an agnostic. I don't know." He was a passive non-believer rather than an active disbeliever—a dissenter but not a deserter from the tenets of the church. "I have been providentially saved from a life of sin," he once remarked whimsically, "by three unorthodox factors—Carlyle, Science, and Love. The philosophy of Carlyle has taught me that a deep sense of religion is quite compatible with the entire absence of theology. Science has given me the support of authority without dogma. Love has opened up to me a view of the sanctity of human nature."

He felt that he needed no other bulwarks against the vicissitudes of this world or of the next—"if, indeed, there *is* a next world." It mattered not at all to him that people called him a heretic, an infidel, and other hard names. He knew that in accordance with the British law the word of a sneak thief who swore on the Bible would be taken against his own word. But he stuck to his honest convictions. "Huxley's passion," said Herbert Spencer, "was not only for truth but for something which is considerably rarer—candor."

His religion was that of a candid skepticism—a constructive rather than a destructive doubt. His attitude toward life was that of the scientist-poet. Truth is wisdom plus beauty. "Teach a child what is wise—that is morality; teach a child what is wise and beautiful—*that* is religion."

V

"TEACH A CHILD what is wise and beautiful." This was the paramount object of Huxley's life. In 1870, thanks to the efforts of Huxley and of other like-minded pioneers, the British Parliament passed an act to offer free education to the children of needy parents. Huxley was elected a member of the new school board. With the pitiless scalpel of his logic he cut deep into the "intellectual snobbishness" of the British aristocracy. "What might not the poor and lowly among men achieve if given the opportunity to education? And what would happen to many others of the 'best' in society? . . . We have all known noble lords who would have been coachmen, or gamekeepers, or billiardmarkers, if they had not been kept afloat by our social corks." In order to preserve a democracy, he declared, you must have not a minority of noble births but a majority of nimble brains.

He dedicated his life to the training of this majority—with his books, his experiments, his lectures. Especially with his lectures. He reveled in his classroom contacts. Here he was at his best. He struck the students speechless with his biting sarcasm. Once he picked up the notebook of an earnest but incompetent Irish student who had been assiduously diagramming a sheep's liver. Huxley studied the drawing for a few moments. "It reminds me," he remarked wryly, "of the Cologne Cathedral in a fog." On another occasion, at the conclusion of a lecture at the blackboard, he asked the men if he had made himself perfectly clear. One bold voice spoke out: "All, sir, but one part during which you stood between me and the blackboard." The professor frowned. "I did my best to make myself clear," he said. "But it seems I couldn't render myself transparent."

Throughout his life he was a whiplash to little minds. Yet the flourish of his wit was worse than its sting. For at bottom he was a gentle soul. And a sick body. He could thank a dyspeptic liver for his sarcastic tongue. As he passed middle age he began to suffer acutely from the "blue devils" of depression and hypochondria.

He took frequent trips to the Mediterranean to fill his lungs with good sea air. But as often as he returned to his professional duties he found his attacks recurring. His friend Hooker had suggested nicotine as an antidote to his gastric disturbances. As a result he became an incessant cigar smoker—but still his digestion remained unimproved.

At fifty-nine he had all his teeth extracted. He feared that this was a grave forewarning. In his zoölogical studies he had noted that the decay of an animal's teeth was a frequent premonition of its death. In his sixtieth year he faded rapidly. He was forced to give up his work on dissection since it entailed too great a demand on his ebbing strength. Once when he was younger he had remarked lightly, "At sixty all scientists should be strangled." He resigned his professorship and his inspectorship at the Department of Fisheries. And finally, with a heavy heart, he gave up the greatest of his honors—the presidency of the Royal Society. In a speech of touching simplicity he explained to the members that in view of all their kindness he could not consider holding the office "for a single moment after my reason and my conscience have pointed out my incapacity to discharge the serious duties of this office." And then, when he had finished the speech he turned to his friends and said in a low voice, "I have just announced my official death."

But he was not as yet ready to die. A new attack had been launched against him and the old lion was ready once more for the fight. The Honorable Mr Gladstone had written in a weekly periodical a bristling denunciation against those who disapproved of the biblical account of the world's creation. The Duke of Argyll had followed up this article with a paper on the "Reign of Terror" instituted by the naturalists who were trying "to destroy the foundations of God."

Instantly Thomas Huxley was cured of all his ailments. A lusty fight was to him the very elixir of life. He took up his pen with his old-time vigor. "The antagonism of science is not to religion, but to the heathen survivals and to the bad philosophy under which religion herself is well-nigh crushed." This had been his lifelong argument. Why this constant attack upon science as the enemy of religion? Science did not reject religion. It merely questioned "this or that philosophical speculation, this or that theological creed." Science had been too long neglected as the poor Cinderella in the respectable family of human culture. "She lights the fire, sweeps the house, and provides the dinner; and is rewarded by being told that she is a base creature, devoted to low and material interests." While her sisters, Philosophy and Theology, are engaged downstairs in a ceaseless quarrel with each other, Science in her garret "has fairy visions beyond their ken." She sees the order which pervades the seeming disorder of the world. She observes the great drama of evolution as it unfolds in its beauty and its terror. And she tries to transform the terror into beauty. It is true that the strong animals prevail over the weak in the jungle. But in the gardens of mankind the meanest flower may be trained to flourish as beautifully as the stateliest tree. "Society differs from nature in having a definite moral object." This doctrine had gradually become Huxley's innermost conviction. "The course shaped by the ethical man—the member of society—necessarily runs counter to that which the non-ethical man—the primitive savage—tends to adopt." When properly understood, both evolution and religion point to the selfsame end—the refinement of brute force into human love.

When Huxley spoke such words as these, the lips of the satyr grew tender with the devotion of the prophet. Here was a philosopher who smote his fellows for their foolishness—out of his great respect for their inherent wisdom. How could they accuse him of wanting to destroy? How could they brand him with a flippant disregard for human faith? Was it impossible for them to conceive of a man who had tasted his share of grief and who at three-score years could still retain the courage to think? "I have graduated in all the faculties of human relationships; I have taken my share in all the deep joys and the deeper anxieties of life . . . I have felt the burden of young lives entrusted to my care . . . I have stood alone with my dead before the abyss of the eternal . . ." This had been his personal struggle for existence. And out of the painful process of gradual adaptation, out of his sanguine youth, his aggressive middle age, his mellow later years—out of all these aspirations and successes and sorrows had come the gradual evolution known as Thomas Huxley. From rash skepticism, to skeptical intelligence—to a final perceptive glimpse. "The thinking man alone can check the natural struggle of brute strength."

And so he entered once more into the arena of thought and

found the vigor of a renewed youth in his winter years. Forgotten was the weakness to which he had yielded in a moment of foolish fear. His energy had caught its second breath. He no longer shuddered at the prospect of physical exertion. On the contrary, he exulted in it. He took a trip to Switzerland (1888) and walked eighteen miles, including a climb of two thousand feet, in a single day. He scoffed at the absurdity of his ever having yielded to "a dilated heart." He made a solemn vow to prolong his labor and to postpone the inevitable end. "For at the end of life all one's work looks so uncommonly small!"

VI

HE BUILT HIMSELF A HOUSE at Beachy Head on the seaside. Like the old philosopher, Candide, he spent his declining years in the cultivation of his garden. And then came the greatest irony into the life of this master of irony. He was canonized into a "respectable institution."

The agnostic had been exalted into a saint. He received the honorary degree of Doctor of Laws from the citadel of British orthodoxy, the University of Cambridge. "I shall be glorious in a red gown!" he wrote sarcastically. He was appointed Dean of the College of Science. "The only ambition that remains to me," he laughed, "is the Archbishopric of Canterbury."

And finally he was knighted. He accepted this honor, like all the others, with his tongue in his cheek. "Ancestral nobility" was to him little more than a farce. "My zoölogical studies have carried me so far back to my remote ancestors that my immediate ancestors no longer interest me."

He never came to court, and he paid but an occasional visit to London. He had grown deaf in one ear and he therefore felt sensitive about accepting social invitations. He never could sit at table, he complained, without making an enemy of the neighbor on his deaf side.

And so he plodded his lonely but cheerful way through his declining years. "There goes Professor Huxley"—once remarked an old lady—"faded but still fascinating."

As he grew older he withdrew more and more from society into the solitude of his garden. When his youngest granddaughter paid him a visit, she looked at him with a puzzled expression in her eyes. "You are the curiousest old man I ever saw!"

A curious man with his curious plants. Here in his garden he inspected his creepers and tended his gentians and sheltered his exposed shrubs against the wind and collected his essays for final publication. The story of progress. From the seed of the past through the growth of the present to the buds and stems of tomorrow.

And what is this hope of tomorrow—this ultimate purpose of the evolutionary process, this gradual acquisition of knowledge through incessant struggling and suffering? Is not the end of all this struggle the survival of the mentally fittest and ethically best? . . .

VII

Huxley passed through a severe winter in his seventieth year. Yet he had never felt more cheerful. The doctors shook their heads, but he laughed at them. As the spring approached, he wrote to his friend Hooker and told him not to pay any attention to the alarming reports that were being published in the newspapers about his health. "I don't feel at all like sending in my checks."

Three days later he was dead.

AGASSIZ

Great Scientific Contributions by Agassiz

Founded the Museum of Comparative Zoölogy at Harvard.

BOOKS, TREATISES AND RESEARCHES:

Species of Fishes (in the Amazon River).

History of the Fresh Water Fishes of Central Europe.

The Growth of Continents.

Researches on Fossil Fishes.

Critical Studies on Fossil Molluscs.

The Structure of Animal Life.

Zoölogical Nomenclature.

The Glacial System.

Geological Sketches.

Agassiz

Louis John Rudolph Agassiz

1807–1873

HE WAS BORN AT MOTIER, a Swiss village nestled on the shore of Lake Morat among the foothills of the Bernese Alps. He came of a Huguenot family which had escaped from France during the persecutions of Louis XIV.

His immediate ancestors on his father's side had been clergymen for six generations. On his mother's side, too, he came of an intellectual—and sturdy—stock. Nature had endowed him with a physical and mental heritage of unusual caliber. He was a man born for action and thought.

From early childhood he developed a passion for collecting fishes and birds and mice and rabbits. His brother Auguste was likewise animated by the collector's mania. The two boys started a home museum of "rare and interesting living things." At fourteen it was the modest aim of Louis, with the help of his brother, to memorize the Latin names "of every known animal and plant." Already he had drawn up a manifesto, which he read to an audience of his own fancy, about his future career as a great scientist.

"I shall advance in the sciences. I shall receive my preliminary training at Neuchatel and matriculate at a university in

Germany. I shall finish my education at Paris. Then I shall begin to write." He was resolved to become an outstanding man of letters.

His parents, to be sure, had other ideas for Louis. They wanted him to join the business firm of his uncle at Neuchatel. But they committed a serious error. At fifteen they allowed him to enter upon a two years' course of study at the College of Lausanne. "Time enough for business later on," they said. They were wrong. From the moment he entered college, Louis Agassiz never changed his allegiance from learning to earning. He had decided upon the course of his life, and in this course he persevered to the end.

II

HE HAD LEARNED that his early ambition to classify all the different species of the plant and the animal kingdoms by merely giving them Latin labels was not enough. He must familiarize himself not only with their names but also and especially with their structures. Then he would be able to follow their classifications and, if necessary, to give them new classifications of his own. He felt that a firsthand observation of nature, even with his unpracticed eye, was worth far more than a stuffy perusal of all the learned Latin treatises on the subject. But if he was to "see for himself where the truth lay" he must wear the proper spectacles. A knowledge of anatomy was the indispensable tool of the naturalist. Accordingly he entered the Medical School at Zurich and came into contact with some of the leading anatomists of the day. He spent many of his waking hours in the dissecting of animals and at night he slept "in a menagerie" of forty birds. He read practically nothing outside of his "living" texts. "The life histories of the feathered songsters were his only novels. The accidental deaths of his pets were his sole tragedies."

Then, Heidelberg. He was nineteen when he appended his name to the students' list at that university. He took fencing lessons to develop the accuracy of his eyes, which were the vital organs of his research. He perfected himself in the Classical and the Romance languages, for a scientist must be at home in all tongues. He rose early and spent every minute of the day purposefully. When the lectures were over he met in his rooms with a party of his fellow students each of whom specialized in some branch of natural history. At these meetings the young "scientific experts" delivered lectures to one another, compared notes and finally organized themselves into a "Little Academy"—a learned society in which "all our members *increase* their knowledge by *sharing* it."

Agassiz had come to believe strongly in this method of educational partnership. "The interchange of notes—that is, the comparative system of education—has opened up to me the philosophical view of nature as one great world." At last he had definitely formulated the plan for his life's work. He would investigate the nature of the world as a comprehensive unit.

But just then the comprehensive unit of his plan received a severe shock. His parents had lost a business man. Now they wanted to find a doctor. They insisted upon his specializing in surgery—a field that would enable him to marry and to settle down to a comfortable living. "The sooner you have completed your medical course," wrote his mother, "the sooner you can pitch your tent, catch your blue butterfly, and transform her into a loving housewife."

There was a stormy controversy between Agassiz and his parents, but at last they reached a compromise. Agassiz might indulge himself in his fish collections provided he practiced surgery as a livelihood. "Let the sciences be the balloon in which you prepare to travel through higher regions, but let medicine and surgery be your parachutes."

Reluctantly the young naturalist began to prepare himself for a profession in which he had little interest when a circumstance arose to save him from his predicament. One of his professors, the eminent scientist Von Martius, invited Agassiz to collaborate with him in a book on natural history which he was preparing for publication. Louis was overwhelmed with excitement. He wrote to his sister Cecile a letter in which he enthusiastically discussed his plans. "Will it not seem strange when the largest and finest book in papa's library is one written by his son, Louis? Will it not be as good as to see my prescription at the apothecary's?"

Even his parents were pleased at the prospect. They heard that the advance sheets of the manuscript had created a sensation among the leading scientists of the day. "Let him play with science for a while, if only he will stick to his medicine as his life's work."

They allowed him to pursue his naturalistic studies until he received the degree of Doctor of Philosophy. Now his name could appear with an academic title on his forthcoming book. Agassiz felt certain of his destiny. Should the book prove a success—and he was confident that it would—his parents would ultimately consent to his adoption of science as his life's vocation. After all, what his parents wanted for him was not necessarily a *medical* but a *successful* career.

With this thought in mind Agassiz set himself indefatigably to his scientific studies. Let other students while away their time in pleasure. He would follow his own course. He would be not merely a great naturalist but the greatest naturalist of his time. The desire to travel in the interests of his studies had come upon him strongly. When he learned that Alexander von Humboldt was looking for assistants to accompany him on an expedition to the Ural Mountains he addressed, with the impulsiveness of youth, a letter to M. Cuvier, the friend of Humboldt, to intercede in his behalf. "For six months I have frequented a blacksmith's and carpenter's shop, learning to handle hammer and axe. And I also practice arms, and exercise with the sabre and the bayonet. I am strong and robust, I know how to swim, and I do not fear forced marches . . . In a word, I seem to myself made to be a traveling naturalist. I need only to regulate the impetuosity which carries me away. I beg you, then, to be my advocate with Herr von Humboldt."

But his petition came too late. Humboldt had already selected his assistants. And Louis Agassiz, to fulfill the promise he had given his parents, continued his medical studies. In spite of his distaste for the profession, he threw himself into these studies with the energy that was part of his natural temper. And he accomplished prodigious results. He wrote more than seventy-five theses on anatomy, surgery, obstetrics and pathology. In April, 1830, Madame Agassiz received the following note from her son: "Dismiss all anxiety about me. You see I am as good as my word." The young man who was already known throughout Europe for his book on natural science had, true to his promise, taken the degree of Doctor of Medicine.

III

HE WENT TO PARIS, the center of scientific learning, and presented himself before Cuvier. The great anatomist received him with open arms. He gave Agassiz a nook in his laboratory and freely bestowed upon him his instruction and advice. The young man had come to Cuvier with a definite purpose. He had heard that the old Frenchman was preparing a book on fossil fishes— a subject which Agassiz himself had been diligently studying for some time. He hoped that when he showed his notes to Cuvier, the latter would commission him to do the entire work. And Agassiz was not disappointed in his hope. Cuvier turned over to him his entire collection of fishes and told him to go ahead with the book. "I work regularly fifteen hours a day," wrote the young scientist to his parents. His small monthly allowance was insufficient to his needs. For he was obliged to hire an artist for the sketching of his specimens. Often he went hungry long before the end of the month. The publisher of a scientific journal, the *Bulletin,* offered him the editorship of the department of zoölogy—a position which would substantially have increased his income. But Agassiz declined the offer. For it would have taken two hours daily from his research. His father begged him to come home and to settle down to surgery. His master Cuvier pleaded with him to relax from his research. "Hard work kills," he warned the young man. The old naturalist was only too well aware of the meaning of these words. Shortly after his warning to Agassiz he was himself stricken with paralysis on his way to the Chamber of Deputies. Within a few days he was dead.

It was a tremendous blow to Agassiz, this loss of his great colleague and friend. Where now would he receive the encouragement to continue his research? His money was as "rare as some of his zoölogical specimens." He must dismiss his artist. He must give up his science. And condemn himself to surgery for life. "If you follow surgery," wrote his mother, "you will perhaps reach the result of your work in the natural sciences a little later." Agassiz knew what that meant. "A little later" was "never."

But again his good fortune came to the rescue in the guise of an old man. This time it was Cuvier's friend, Alexander von Humboldt, who acted the part of the Good Samaritan. Agassiz had called upon the illustrious scientist shortly after his arrival at Paris, and Humboldt had promised to write to the publisher, Cotta, regarding the manuscript which the young man was preparing. For several weeks there was no word either from Humboldt or from the publisher—weeks of hunger, privation, despair. And then at last Agassiz received a response—a letter that was quite different from anything he had expected. It contained a check for a thousand francs! The old scientist had learned of the young scientist's plight. "You will surely pardon my friendly good will toward you, my dear M. Agassiz, if I entreat you to make use of the accompanying small credit," he wrote in words of exquisite tact. "You would do more for me, I am sure."

This was but an initial step in Humboldt's sponsorship or Agassiz. He used his influence to obtain for the junior naturalist a professorship at the Swiss university of Neuchatel. And so Agassiz returned home—and not as a surgeon. His parents were now completely won over to the thought that their son could make a good living even as a scientist.

IV

HIS SUCCESS as a natural historian was assured. Installed as a teacher at the university, he had become an immediate favorite both with the faculty and with the students. He had gained the patronage of Humboldt, and through him the admiration of the king of Prussia. At twenty-five he had transformed Neuchatel by the magic of his personality and his talent into a great center of science. His colleagues throughout Europe were impressed by the intense energy of his researches. "When I am at Neuchatel and knock at the door of Agassiz," jestingly remarked the geologist, Leopold von Buch, "I am always afraid lest he will take me for a new species."

Agassiz did not confine his energy to his teaching and his studies. He was a great lover of children, and the children shared his great love for nature. He enjoyed firing their imagination as he strolled with them through the hills and the fields and talked to them of the works of God. Never did he believe in a textbook illustration of the beauty of nature. His was a living science, waiting to be unfolded to the eyes of all. He taught his little colleagues the elements of geography by climbing with them a mountain and pointing out the vast panorama below. He initiated them into the mysteries of botany while they gathered the flowers of the field. When he gave them a lesson on the tropical fruits he presented them with oranges and bananas and invited them to eat these fruits while he explained their structure. The children looked upon him not as their instructor but as their playmate. He was as full of gaiety as the most frolicsome of his little pupils.

He had introduced a new method of education. He had renounced the stuffy classroom and returned to the gardens of the old Greek philosophers. And like the old Greek philosophers he was not only an assiduous teacher but a persevering student as well. Every moment that he could spare from his pupils he devoted to his own researches. For a time indeed it seemed that he had overexerted himself to his serious injury. The doctors feared that he was becoming permanently blind. But even that affliction did not deter him from his work. For hours he sat in a darkened room and practiced handling his fossil specimens until he acquired so delicate a sense of touch that he no longer feared his impending blindness. "Come what may, I shall be able to go on with my research."

But the fates, having tested him, gave him back his sight. And then he plunged more enthusiastically than ever into his work. His fame spread all over continental Europe and beyond. The leading naturalists of England invited him to examine their collections of fossil specimens. As a result of his original research in *ichthyology* (the science of fishes), Sir Charles Lyell informed him that he had won the Wollaston prize—a sizable sum of money which he did not hesitate to accept since he had spent "his last penny" on this research. He made a trip to England and received a cordial welcome. He had become the toast of the scientific world.

Yet there were some who remained skeptical about his genius. These skeptics maintained that there was more froth than substance to his scientific claims. And they decided to put him to the test. A fossil fish had just been discovered in a stratum so low and indicative of so remote an epoch that it had thus far yielded no other specimens of organic remains. Agassiz, who had not as yet heard of the discovery of the fish, was invited to a gathering of the skeptics and confronted with a question designed to lead him into a trap. If given a certain low geologic stratum, he was asked, could he venture to describe the type of fish that might be found there? For a moment the Swiss naturalist was silent. Then he went to the blackboard and after a few prefatory remarks in which he discussed the laws and the order of creation he sketched the outlines of the "hypothetical" fish that might be found in such a given stratum. When the fossil that had actually been discovered was now brought forward and compared with the sketch, the audience burst into a thunder of applause. For the conception of Agassiz was absolutely correct. "This man," exclaimed one of the amazed spectators, "has unearthed the very plans of God as if by a miracle!"

There was nothing of the miraculous, however, in the scientific method of Agassiz. He had merely learned to read the world as intelligently as some of the other scientists had learned to read their books. To his mental as well as to his physical eye the world presented an organic structure. It told a logical story, and anyone could learn to understand its related parts. Even as a young student he had learned that the study of the bodily structure of animals must be related to the study of the bodily structure of the earth. "Geology is but an extension of zoölogy."

It was not surprising, therefore, that Agassiz turned from fossils to glaciers. He wandered over the valley of the Rhone and he climbed the boulders of the Juras. He lived in a cabin pitched upon a glacier that was churned again and again by a tempest of pulverized ice. Together with his party he struggled over vast terraces, sinking into the snow, tiptoeing over thin layers of ice, spanning crevasses that looked bottomless, scaling cliffs and clinging to life by a slender rope. And thus gradually "all the physical laws of the glaciers were brought to light."

At one point Agassiz had determined to descend into the heart of the glacier—a feat which had been accomplished by no man before him. His companions protested vigorously against the dangerous project, but in the end they were compelled to give in to his obstinacy. They lowered him into a glacial well in a mass that was moving at the rate of forty feet a day. It was an even chance that Agassiz might remain buried forever in this frozen grave. Out of sight he sank seated upon a board. The deeper he descended the more intense the gloom. He was fascinated by the blue bands of ice that ran around the walls of the pit—a greenish blue at the top and a midnight blue below. When he reached a depth of eighty feet he found a wall of ice that divided the passage into two tunnels. He selected one of the tunnels and continued his descent to a depth of one hundred and twenty feet. Suddenly he found himself plunged into cold water. He signaled to be hoisted immediately, but his companions misunderstood the signal. They continued lowering him—to certain death, as he thought. Once more he shouted and this time he was understood. As he began his ascent he saw huge icicles that pointed at him from above and threatened at every moment to transfix him. It was a tremulous and breathless philosopher that finally came to the surface amidst the cheers of his friends.

But this narrow escape did not deter him from further adventures in the interests of science. From the Alps he went on to study the glacial formations of the Scottish highlands. And finally he published an account of his geologic investigations. He advanced the theory—regarded as revolutionary in the scientific circles of the day—that Europe at one stage had been completely covered by a solid sheet of ice. "Siberian winter established itself for a time over a world previously filled with a rich vegetation . . . Death enveloped all nature in a shroud . . . Springs paused; rivers ceased to flow; the rays of the sun, rising upon this frozen shore . . . were met only by the breath of the winter from the north and by the thunders of the crevasses as they opened across the surface of this mighty ocean of ice."

His book on the glacial period, *Le Système Glaciaire,* proved to be as monumental a contribution in the field of geology as his works on fossil fishes had been in the field of ichthyology. And his reputation increased proportionately—not only among the savants, but among the common people as well. On one of his trips with a party of friends he stopped on the road for refreshment. An elderly traveler overheard the name "Agassiz" and came over to the youngish-looking individual who had been addressed by that name.

"Pardon me, but are you the son of the celebrated Professor Agassiz of Neuchatel?"

Agassiz smiled, and one of his companions remarked, "You are standing before Professor Agassiz himself."

The stranger turned away with an apology, and one of the bystanders heard him whisper to himself: "Such a modest young body for such a wise old head!"

The admiration for this "wise old head" was nowhere greater than in America. The trustees of the Lowell Institute invited him to deliver a course of lectures in Boston. Agassiz was only too happy to accept the invitation. The idea of a trip to the new continent in the interest of science had long been one of his "unattainable" dreams. And here was his dream unexpectedly come true!

When the popular young professor left for America the little university town of Neuchatel was plunged in gloom. To be sure, Agassiz had promised that he would return; but there were many who feared that he might succumb to the fascinations of the New World.

Yet they all rejoiced in his good luck, and they wished him a hearty *bon voyage*. The Prussian king presented him with a gift of fifteen thousand francs. And the king of all the scientists sent him a godspeed message written in a hand that trembled with age. "Be happy in your new undertaking, and preserve for me the first place in your heart. When you return I shall be here no more, but the king and the queen will receive you on this 'historic hill' of Sans Souci with the affection which, for so many reasons, you merit. . . . Your illegible but much attached friend—Alexander von Humboldt."

V

AGASSIZ was thirty-nine years old when he arrived in Boston (October, 1846). He fell an immediate and willing captive to the charm of American democracy. "A characteristic feature of

American life," he wrote to a friend in Europe, "is to be found in the frequent public meetings where addresses are delivered. Shortly after my arrival in Boston I was present at a meeting of some three thousand workmen, foremen of workshops, clerks and the like. No meeting could have been more respectable or better conducted. All were neatly dressed; even the simplest laborer had a clean shirt. It was a strange sight to see such an assemblage, brought together for the purpose of forming a library, and listening attentively in perfect quiet for two hours to an address on the advantages of education."

He was a European who spoke broken English. Yet in the language of the heart he already felt himself a native of the great republic. He was perfectly at home among the American people. "What a people! . . . In the Old World a man of exceptional gifts is content to devote himself to a lifetime of cloistered study while at his side thousands of his fellow men vegetate in degradation . . . Here in the New World everybody lives well, is decently clad, learns something, is awake and interested . . . Instruction does not—as in some parts of Germany, for instance —furnish a man with an intellectual tool and then deny him the free use of it. In America all men are allowed to employ their talents for the common good . . ."

But if he found among the general masses an eagerness for learning he found also among the intellectuals a high standard of scholarship. At Harvard College, whose faculty he joined within a year after his arrival in Boston, he met a group of teachers whose brilliancy could hardly be matched anywhere in Europe. Among his intimate colleagues at this University-on-the-Charles were such men as Longfellow, Felton, Pierce, Wyman and Asa Gray. His wider circle of friends included Channing and Emerson, Ticknor, Motley, Whittier and Lowell. Small wonder, then, that Agassiz felt little inclination to go home.

And now the final tie that linked him with his former home was broken. His wife died. He sent for his children, married an

American woman and settled down to the business of transforming his adopted country into the scientific center of the world.

But his old country did not give him up without a struggle. The trustees of the University of Zurich appealed to him as "a good European" to return home. And they held out a remunerative professorship as a bait. The Emperor Napoleon "commanded" him as a French citizen to come back to Paris and to accept a position at the *Jardin des Plantes*. To the Zurich request he replied gently that his obligation to his new country was of more moment to his conscience than his affiliation with the old; to the emperor's demand he replied more sternly that he was not a French citizen, although his ancestry was of French origin. "For centuries my family has been Swiss, and in spite of my ten years' exile I am still Swiss." Swiss by birth, but American by affection. America was to become the home of his most ardent dream—a museum of natural history.

When he had first arrived in Cambridge he had stored his precious collections in an old building on the college grounds. For a short time he had left Harvard to accept a professorship at the Charleston Medical School and a fear for the safety of his specimens had haunted him throughout his absence. When he returned to Harvard he was determined to find an adequate shelter for them in a permanent museum.

But his plans for a museum had now grown far beyond the exigencies of his personal interests. This treasure house of the ages was to become the embodiment of his life's philosophy. Here the student would find his laboratory and here too the layman would see spread out before him an exhibition of specimens so arranged that each individual part of nature would at once show its intimate relationship to the whole—"an epitome, as it were, of the Creation." So ran his dream. Ardently he discussed it with his friends, with the light of prophecy in his eye and a prophetic enthusiasm on his lips.

And then one of his friends died and left him fifty thousand dollars for the establishment of the museum. Agassiz accepted this bequest, but only on one condition—that the proposed institute be known not as the *Agassiz Museum* but merely as the *Museum of Comparative Zoölogy at Harvard*. It now remained for the Massachusetts legislature to vote a grant of land. Some of the assemblymen were rather skeptical about the construction of a "palace for bugs." But they voted the grant.

The museum was erected as a "gateway to the world of science" and as an embodiment of the doctrines of the Swiss professor. Here he was master over the vast universe of the mind as he led his students, step by step, down the illuminated aisles of the centuries. With the fervor of a poet he taught the tenets of his scientific creed—"I believe."

VI

AGASSIZ RENOUNCED the Darwinian conception of evolution which affirmed that the development of living organisms came about wholly through *natural selection from accidental variations*. He could not, like Darwin, conclude that "the development from the lower to the higher, from the simple to the complex" was merely a mechanical and material process. On the contrary, he believed that this development was the result of the highest ethical forces forever at work in the universe. The Darwinians had banished all purpose in the life of the individual. The only law they recognized was the organic law of physical force. This, maintained Agassiz, is the hopeless conception of a godless world. "Evolution," he said, "takes place not according to organic forces within but according to an intelligent plan without."

This challenge to the Darwinian theory of evolution was fundamental. Once the doctrine of divine creation is superseded by the dogma of natural selection, man has been robbed of his spirit and reduced to an automaton with mechanical wheels for a soul. Agassiz intuitively foresaw the destructive consequences of the Darwinian theory if carried to its inexorable conclusion.

The too literal interpretation—or rather misinterpretation—of this theory was destined to give rise to the Superman of Friedrich Nietzsche and to the exaltation of physical force as the only basis for conduct among men.

Many of Agassiz' pupils, for want of scientific evidence, rejected their teacher's doctrine of a divine guidance. But Agassiz was a teacher not only of science but of ethics. His observations tended to convince him that the Darwinian theory of the transmutation of the species was incorrect. There was a distinct difference, he felt, between the *generation* of a species and the *creation* of a species. The Darwinian biologists had never stepped beyond the physical laws of generation to the causes for creation. "Animals can generate—that is, reproduce—their kind; God alone can create a new kind." This he firmly believed. "The idea of the procreation of a new species by a preceding species is a gratuitous supposition opposed to all sound physiological notions." He found it impossible to believe that the "biological phenomena, which have been and still are going on upon the surface of our globe, are due to the simple action of physical forces. I believe they are due, in their entirety, as well as individually, to the direct intervention of a creative power, acting freely and in an autonomic way . . . I am certain that there is not only a material connection but also and especially an intellectual coherence in things. . . . This intentional plan I have tried to make evident in the organization of the animal kingdom . . ." This was the dream of his museum, the sole purpose of his teaching—to give back to man his lost understanding of God.

Formally Agassiz had the mind of a metaphysician. Actually he was a hard-headed pragmatist in his method of instruction. When he was asked to cite what he regarded as his greatest achievement he replied, "Observation. I have taught men to observe." To the uninitiated pupil who first came to his classes his teaching was difficult. He would place before his pupil the skeleton of an old loon or the body of a smelly fish and tell him to note down his observations about the specimen. Then he would leave him to his task without a word of advice or a question or a comment. When he returned he would merely ask with a friendly smile, "Well, what have you seen?" When the pupil finished describing his observations, Agassiz would reply, "That is not enough. Go back to your specimen and look some more."

Look, look, look—was his constant injunction. To look was to know. From all those who wanted to study nature under his supervision he exacted the same toil that he had imposed upon himself. But this toil had at last begun to tell on him. The splendid constitution that had enabled him to sleep night after night on a glacier with only a blanket under him, to stumble up the peaks of mountains and to descend into the depths of icy caverns—all in the interests of science—was now beginning to fail him. His old master, Cuvier, had uttered prophetic words when he had said that "work kills." His friends urged him to take a vacation. And the devotee of learning took their advice in characteristic fashion. He left the museum at Cambridge for the tropics of Brazil. He exchanged his teaching engagement for a trip of exploration to collect specimens of the fresh-water fishes in the South American rivers. Never did he work more strenuously than during this "vacation." He delivered lectures on the steamer that took him to South America. When he arrived there he worked from early morning till late at night gathering and arranging his specimens. And when he returned to the United States he delivered a course of lectures at Cooper Union, in New York City, on the results of his trip.

And then he went back to add his new specimens to the collections of his beloved museum. Here was another group of links binding more closely together the chain of evidence that the order of nature was not mechanical but purposeful, not the accident of a blind force but the design of a Supreme Intellect. For Agassiz regarded his scientific vocation as a priesthood. His museum was his cathedral; and it was here that the modern scientist carried on the work of the ancient prophets. "It is the business of the prophets and the scientists alike to declare the glory of God."

VII

AT LAST the prophet-scientist had worn himself out completely with his labors. He suffered a paralytic stroke. The doctors prescribed "a long rest" in the country. They never expected him to recover. But again the fighter who all his life had struggled against odds came out victorious in the unequal battle. Within a few months he was back at Cambridge. He appeared to be in perfect health again. He received and accepted an offer to make a scientific cruise to the Pacific. When he reached Santiago he learned that the French had elected him foreign associate of the Institute. "The distinction pleased me the more because it was so unexpected," he wrote to a friend. And then he added with a touch of whimsical sadness, "Unhappily . . . it is to a house in ruins that the diploma is addressed."

Yet in spite of the premonition of his approaching end, his active mind was still preoccupied with great projects. He had long been planning a summer school where teachers of nature might undertake scientific investigations under his guidance. But he had no capital for such an undertaking. "In the course of my life," he had once remarked, "I have found time for everything except for making money." Fortunately a wealthy admirer in New York, Mr John Anderson, presented him with a tract of land on Buzzard's Bay together with a substantial sum of money for the proposed summer school. On July 4, 1873, Agassiz set sail for Buzzard's Bay with all the enthusiasm of youth. The spirit in the man refused to die.

When he arrived on the island he found that the work on the buildings was as yet far from completed, although the students chosen for the class were expected to arrive in a few days. Undaunted, Agassiz called the carpenters together. "There is no personal gain involved in this school. There is no money to be made. Its one purpose is to promote education. We are confronted with an emergency. Tomorrow is Sunday. It is up to you to decide whether you work or rest."

"We work!"

When the boat from New Bedford arrived with its cargo of young men and women the dormitories were ready to receive them. The barn had been transformed into a reception hall; the platform was covered with flowers; and the walls were brightly festooned with silk draperies. On the wharf as the students disembarked stood the old Professor alone. His great face beamed with pleasure; his white hair glistened in the sun. He gathered his students around him and paused in silent prayer.

Agassiz returned to Cambridge in the fall. The sands of his allotted time had nearly run out. He prepared to write for the *Atlantic Monthly* a series of articles defending his theories on evolution. But he could hardly steady himself for the effort. He hadn't the strength to face the coming winter. It was getting dark and late. "I want to rest," he said. "I am tired; I am ready to go."

At times as he trudged to and from the museum he felt a strange drowsiness. He was sleep-walking in a world he no longer recognized. But whenever he opened his eyes and saw again the life around him, his heart sang a silent psalm to the Creative God whom he knew and adored.

Then late one day in December he put away his specimens for the last time. And men grieved for the family and the friends he left behind him. But no one grieved for Louis Agassiz. "There was little of him that could die."

MENDEL

Great Scientific Contribution by Mendel

Discovered and formulated the
Mendelian Laws of
Heredity.

TREATISE:
Plant Hybridization.

Mendel

Gregor Johann Mendel

1822–1884

I N THE SPRING OF 1850 Gregor Johann Mendel presented himself for examination as a high school teacher at Altbrünn. He had already taught for some time as a substitute teacher, but he was anxious to secure a permanent appointment. "The respectful undersigned," he wrote in his application, "would deem himself happy if he should be able to satisfy the highly respected examiners, and thus to fulfil his desire."

But Mendel was not able to satisfy "the highly respected examiners." They "ploughed" him in natural science. "The candidate," wrote the examiners, "has not mastered this subject sufficiently to qualify him as a teacher in the higher schools."

Disappointed in his first attempt, Mendel went back to his textbooks and several months later presented himself for a second examination. Again the examiners "flunked" him. "This (second) examination paper would hardly allow us to regard the candidate as competent to become an instructor even in the lower schools."

Such was the verdict of the contemporary "experts" on the scientific ability of one of history's outstanding scientists.

II

MENDEL'S FAILURE in his examinations was due to his originality. He wrote above the heads of his examiners. "This candidate," they complained, "pays no attention to technical terminology. He uses his own words and expresses his own ideas instead of relying upon traditional knowledge."

But Mendel continued to use his own words and to express his own ideas. For he came of a stubborn and tenacious stock. For generations the Mendels had stuck to their guns and insisted upon their rights. On more than one occasion they had defied the authorities who had tried to impose their arbitrary will upon them. It was in the Mendel blood to select a course of action, or to enter upon a train of thought, and to pursue it to the end in spite of all opposition or failure.

And the course of action that Gregor had selected was to discover and to demonstrate some of the hidden secrets of nature. To discover these secrets not out of the textbooks but out of the heart of nature herself.

Mendel's love for nature, like his tenacity of purpose, came to him from several generations of peasants and gardeners. Born in the Moravian village of Heinzendorf, "the flower of the Danube," he was brought up with a passion for growing things. His father, a peasant by profession, was a horticulturist by inclination. Mendel spent many an hour of his childhood tending the plants in his father's garden.

Tending the plants, and observing them. He developed an early love for study. "Just what is it that gives the colors and the shapes to the different trees and fruits and flowers?" Fortunately he was able to learn something about these secrets in his elementary schooling. For the Countess of Waldburg, the lady of the Heinzendorf manor, had insisted upon the introduction of the study of nature as part of the curriculum in the schools of the district. The school inspector, Pater Friedl, referred to this scientific study of nature in the elementary schools as a "scandal." But, luckily for Mendel's future development as a natural scientist, the Countess of Waldburg refused to eliminate this "scandal" from the Heinzendorf schools.

Following his elementary training at Heinzendorf, Mendel entered the high school at the neighboring town of Troppau. He worked his way through the six classes of the high school on "half rations." For his parents were unable to finance him to three square meals a day. As a result of his privations, he fell seriously ill (in 1839) and was compelled to interrupt his studies for several months.

His poverty and his illness threatened to put an end to his studies altogether, when a piece of good luck came to him in the shape of ill luck to his father. One winter day, as his father was chopping down a tree, the trunk fell upon his chest and partially crushed it. Unable to go on with his work on the farm, he sold it to the husband of his eldest daughter, Veronika, and gave a substantial part of the proceeds to his other two children, Johann and Theresia. The sum given to Theresia was meant as her dowry, but the young girl generously turned every penny of it over to Johann. Encouraged by this gift, Johann took up the study of philosophy at the Olmütz Institute and after four years of hard study, occasional illness and perpetual hunger he was ready to enter upon his life's career.

But here was a perplexing question. Just what was Mendel's career to be? "It is incumbent upon me," he wrote, "to enter a profession in which I may be spared perpetual anxiety about a means of livelihood." He went to one of his teachers, Professor Michael Franz, and asked his advice about this matter. Professor Franz recommended a monastic life as best suited to meet his pupil's requirements. And so, on October 9, 1843, Mendel entered the Augustinian monastery at Altbrünn, assumed the name of Gregor, and settled down to a life of prayerful devotion and practical toil.

III

SHORTLY before Mendel's arrival at Altbrünn a botanical garden had been planted on the monastery grounds under the supervision of one of the monks, Father Aurelius Thaler, a botanist noted for his profound learning, spiritual fervor and capacious thirst. Father Thaler was in the habit of following up a hard day in the garden with a merry evening at the tavern. Displeased with this friar's excessive love for the winecup the abbot of the monastery, Father Cyril Napp, decided one night to teach him a lesson. Decking himself out with all the insignia of his office, he sat down to wait for the erring member of his fold in the porter's lodge. It was not until late in the night when the wayward friar knocked for admission. His imagination, like his tongue, had been highly stimulated by "the cup that gladdens the heart." At the sight of his chief all dressed in his "heavenly regalia" he was for a moment flabbergasted. But he quickly pulled himself together. With a deep and reverential bow he addressed himself to the abbot: "Lord, I am not worthy to come under thy roof." Then he turned on his heel—and went back to the tavern.

This merry "godson of Friar Tuck" died just before Mendel came to the monastery. But he left behind him not only the memory of a pleasant personality but also the legacy of a well stocked and scientifically tended garden. This garden was to Mendel like a gift from above. Here he spent all his spare moments, "watching and nursing the plants from their infancy to their old age." And in this botanical interest Mendel was not alone. Several of his fellow monks, sons of peasants like himself, shared his love for scientific gardening. It was a congenial group in which he now found himself—congenial not only temperamentally but intellectually as well. In their evenings they discussed theology, literature, philosophy, science, and occasionally even politics. For those were the revolutionary days of the eighteen-forties. Men were opening their minds to new thoughts and their hearts to new visions. Even in the sheltered retreats of the monasteries these new thoughts and new visions had begun to take root. Some of Mendel's associates left the monastery for the larger world, since they preferred to fight rather than to pray for their fellow men.

As for Mendel, the revolutionary current swept him along for a while and then left him behind. He was a student rather than a fighter. In spite of his peasant tenacity—a tenacity which we shall see most vigorously displayed in his later years—he was too sensitive a soul for the blows and the bloodlettings of the everyday world. He couldn't bear to see suffering. He tried for a time to serve as a parish priest, but his superiors found him unfitted for this work, "the reason being that he is seized by an unconquerable anguish when he is obliged to visit the bed of a sick or a dying person . . . Indeed, this infirmity of his has made him dangerously ill, and that is why we have found it necessary to relieve him from service as a parish priest."

And so Mendel returned to his monastery and his garden. But he was dissatisfied with the passive life of the monastic order. His temperament was too energetic for mere contemplation. It craved for action as well. Mendel's was not only the receptive but also the instructive type of mind. He wanted to teach as well as to study. He applied for a position as substitute teacher in the local high school and got the job at a substitute's salary—that is, 60 per cent of the amount paid to the regular teachers.

His work at the school was satisfactory, his demeanor kindly, and his conduct "reputable—except for the fact that he has on six occasions been to the theater." However, the school authorities were inclined to wink at this "aberration" on his part. After all, they admitted, "he has never gone to the theater alone, but always in the society of one of his colleagues." In spite of his "fondness for mummery," they concluded, "he is competent enough to serve as a substitute teacher."

As a substitute, but not as a permanent teacher. For the examiners, as we have already seen, had decided that he was too ignorant a scholar to be entrusted professionally with the instruction of the young. He remained an "amateur" teacher to the end of his days.

IV

MENDEL'S TEACHING did not interfere with his monastic duties at Altbrünn. He continued to live at the cloister and to cultivate the plants in its garden. He was a jovial, short and stocky little fellow, with a high forehead, a wide and generous mouth, a healthy appetite and a hearty laugh. His gray-blue eyes looked out through their glasses with a perpetual twinkle of cordial good will. He was a contented spirit in a beautiful world. Yet there were times when his contentment gave way to indignation. The world was beautiful, but man was doing his best to make it ugly. The dreams of the creators were all too frequently crushed by the ambitions of the destroyers. The Prussians had invaded Austria (1866) and their yoke lay heavy upon the inhabitants of the conquered land. "The Prussians entered Brünn on July 12," wrote Mendel to his brother-in-law, Leopold Schindler, "and their billeting was extremely oppressive ... Horses, cows, sheep and fowls were carried off in great numbers; so were fodder and grain—with the result that even well-to-do landowners have been reduced almost to beggary . . . The (invading) soldiers occupy the beds, while the regular inhabitants are compelled to lie on the floor or to sleep in the stable."

But the evil of the Prussian invasion passed, and Mendel was able to go on undisturbed with his work. He had become interested in the cross fertilization of the common pea. "Out of the simplest things shall ye know the truth." Mendel hoped, through his study of the heredity of plants, to learn something about the secret of the heredity of man. "How can we explain the manifold shapes and colors of living things?" In order to find a possible answer to this question, he asked for a little plot of land in the monastery garden and proceeded to transform this plot into a living textbook. He selected twenty-two varieties of the edible pea—varieties differing in shape, size and color—and for seven years he mated, remated and transmated them and carefully noted the characteristics of their "children."

And this, in brief, is the summary of the characteristics he discovered in the successive generations of the "children of the garden":

1. When two different types of plants (or of animals) are mated, all the offspring of the next generation will be alike. This he called *the law of uniformity*.

For example, if you cross a red flower with a white flower, all the offspring will be gray.

2. When the uniform offspring of the different plants are mated, the resulting offspring will *not* be uniform, but will segregate themselves into different forms according to a definite numerical ratio. This he called *the law of segregation*.

For example, if you cross the gray flowers that have sprung from the crossing of the red flower and the white flower, you will get the following results:

Out of every eight offspring, two will be red, two will be white, and four will be gray. The crossing of the red flowers of this generation will always produce *red flowers*. The crossing of the white flowers of this generation will always produce *white flowers*. But the crossing of the gray flowers of this generation like the crossing of the previous generation of gray flowers, will out of every eight offspring produce *two red flowers, two white flowers, and four gray flowers*. And all these flowers in turn will act in accordance with the Mendelian law of segregation. The reds will produce only reds, the whites will produce only whites, and the grays will produce reds and whites and grays in the proportion of two reds to two whites to four grays. This law of proportional segregation will hold true of every successive generation of the "inter-marriage" of plants or of animals or of human beings.

The above is a somewhat loose and simplified explanation of the Mendelian laws of heredity. The crossing of two different breeds does not always produce an intermediate breed. If, for example, you mate a black dog with a tawny dog, you will most likely get a litter not of brown dogs but of black dogs. But all the dogs in this first litter will be *uniformly* black, and all the dogs in the interbreeding of this litter will be *segregated* into black, tawny and brown in the ratio of two to two to four. Thus the Mendelian laws of absolute uniformity as a result of the breeding of two different types, and of proportional segregation as a result of the interbreeding of hybrid (or mixed breed) types, will still hold true.

V

Such was the mathematical design of nature that Mendel discovered in the laws of the physical inheritance of living and growing things. It took him seven years of patient research to make this discovery. And it took the world thirty years to realize that a great new discovery had been made. When he first read his paper on *Plant Hybridization* before the Altbrünn Society for the Study of Natural Science, his audience listened politely, applauded faintly and promptly forgot the whole thing. He published the paper, and it lay neglected on the dusty shelves of a few libraries. Disheartened at this universal apathy toward his scientific efforts, he went back to his monastic duties and his teaching. In the cloister and the classroom at least he received a measure of recognition for his labors. Indeed he was rather popular with his fellow friars and his pupils.

Especially with his pupils. They liked their rotund and jolly little teacher—his figure had filled out substantially as a result of the plentiful rich food at the monastery—and they came eagerly to his classes, not so much to imbibe his knowledge as to chuckle over his anecdotes. He told them about the funny antics of his "children"—the plants and the insects and the animals which he kept in his garden and his cloister for his experiments. He related to them how one night, when he was asleep, his pet hedgehog had crept into one of his top boots. "Imagine my surprise in the morning when I tried to put on my boot and my big toe stepped upon a thousand needles!" He frequently invited his pupils into the monastery where he acquainted them at first hand with the habits of his bees and his birds and his mice. Whenever the circus came to town, he took his entire class along with him to have a little "chat" with the animals. One of these "chats" came near to proving rather serious to Mendel. In his effort to attract the attention of the monkeys in one of the cages, he got too close to the bars. Whereupon the largest of the monkeys snatched off his spectacles. It was only with difficulty, and at the expense of a number of painful scratches, that Mendel succeeded in persuading the animal to give up his glasses. In spite of his pain, he had a good laugh together with his pupils over his comical "wrestling" match with the monkey.

His pupils admired this good-natured sort of humor that could laugh at its own discomfiture. But most of all they admired his gentleness. His impartial smile served alike to compliment the brilliant and to encourage the stupid among his pupils. Remembering his own grief at his failure to pass his examinations, he rarely allowed any of his pupils to suffer a setback. Toward the end of the term he asked whether any of them wanted better marks. Then he would allow them to question one another. Naturally each of them would be as lenient as possible toward his neighbor in the hope of an equal lenience in return. To those of his pupils who still fell behind after this friendly cross questioning he extended an invitation to come to the monastery garden for special tuition without pay.

Finally, however, he was obliged to give up his teaching. For he received a new honor which required new duties. He was elected abbot of the monastery at Altbrünn.

VI

ONE OF MENDEL'S FIRST ACTS as the new prelate of Altbrünn was to return the kindness of his sister, Theresia, who had given up her dowry in order that he might go on with his education. He now repaid her with the education of her three sons, assuming the entire expense of their high school and college training. And even to strangers he was lavish with his purse. His gifts for the most part were anonymous. "There is no sense in humiliating the beneficiary by advertising yourself as his benefactor." Though he enjoyed a substantial salary as head of the cloister, he proved to his own satisfaction the adage that "it is more blessed to give than to receive."

Prelate Mendel loved to give and he loved to live. He always entertained his friends—out of his own pocket—at the monastery. On festival occasions, such as the Corpus Christi day and the day of St Thomas, he kept open house and larder to the entire village. As for his Christmas celebrations, they were like "a succession of enchantments out of the Arabian Nights."

And yet he lived to taste the bitter fruits of unpopularity. For he entered upon a course of action which, though it seemed to him justified, was nevertheless stubborn and in the opinion of many of his acquaintances ill advised. The Reichsrat had passed a bill (1874) for the taxation of church property "in order to supply the financial needs of religious worship, and especially in order to increase the salaries of parish priests." Mendel regarded this bill as unconstitutional and refused to pay the tax on the monastery at Altbrünn. Instead he offered to send a "voluntary contribution" to the state treasury, "since I do not close my eyes to the fact that an increase in the Moravian religious fund is necessary."

The state refused to accept the contribution and Mendel refused to pay the tax. For several years the obstinate struggle went on. In turn the government tried to persuade him with promises of promotion and to intimidate him with threats of punishment. But Mendel refused to be either cajoled or frightened. His intimate friends advised him to give in. Mendel's only reply was to accuse these friends of having turned against him. He regarded himself as a "lonely crusader struggling for the right." The state, on the other hand, looked upon him as a "foolish old man who refuses to obey the law."

As the years advanced and the struggle remained undecided, Mendel began to suffer from a pathological irritability. He complained before his nephews that he was persecuted. "There is a plan being concocted to send me to a lunatic asylum."

Such was the clouded and embittered atmosphere in which he spent the remaining years of his life. His one desire was to live to see the day when the "obnoxious law" against his monastery would be revoked. This desire was not destined to be fulfilled. In the spring of 1883 he suffered a heart attack. He recovered partially from this attack, and spent the last few months of his life "among his flowers and his birds and his bees." He had attached a wire cage to the monastery beehives and he had placed a number of bees in that cage. When one of his visitors asked him the reason for this "segregation" of the bees he explained jestingly: "I have put a queen there, together with a number of drones. The queen is choosing a proper husband, for it is just as unfortunate among bees as it is among human beings when a good woman is mated to a bad man." He was still experimenting with the laws of life though he knew that his own life was at an end.

The end came on January 6, 1884. A great concourse of people mourned the passing of a lovable though rather obstinate old priest. But not a single one of the mourners realized that a supreme scientist had just passed away.

PASTEUR

Great Scientific Contributions by Pasteur

Researches in fermentation.

Discovered remedies for silkworm diseases, chicken cholera, anthrax, etc.

Introduced the process known as *pasteurization*.

Established the germ theory in animal and human diseases.

Instituted the practice of disinfection in surgical operations and of inoculation against hydrophobia.

Pasteur

Louis Pasteur

1822–1895

He is the meekest, smallest and least promising pupil in my class," wrote the schoolteacher of Louis Pasteur. But the youngster had an insatiable curiosity. "Let me remind you," observed his teacher one day, "that it's the pupil's business not to *ask* questions but to *answer* them."

And he possessed another rare quality—a patient tenacity for work. "The three most important words in the dictionary," he wrote while still in his early teens, "are—*will, work, wait*. These are the three cornerstones upon which I shall build the pyramid of my success."

II

The son of a tanner, he got the smell of the leather in his blood. Once, when he was ill and homesick while studying at the *École Normale* in Paris, he wrote to his father: "If I could only catch a whiff of the tannery once more, I'm sure I'd get well."

From the smell of the tannery to the "odors of the laboratory" was but a step. From earliest childhood he had made up his mind to be a chemist. "Too bad he's wasting his time on this useless science," said the villagers of Arbois to his father. But

Pasteur *père* had faith in his son. "I know I can depend upon Louis to do the right thing."

Yet even his father had begun to have his doubts when Pasteur received his Bachelor of Science degree with nothing better than a "mediocre" in chemistry. "Just be patient and trust me," wrote the unsuccessful student to his father. "I shall do better as I go on."

And he went on to study for his doctorate in chemistry. In order to earn his expenses he accepted a number of private pupils, teaching them from five to seven in the morning. And in order to stretch his earnings as far as possible he rationed his food, his recreation and his firewood down to the bare level of subsistence. He frequently suffered from hunger pangs. "But fortunately I was also subject to frequent headaches, so that the one pain tended to cancel out the other."

During this period he received further fuel to his ambition in the lectures of the great chemist, J. B. Dumas. "You cannot imagine the popularity of these lectures," he wrote to his father. "M. Dumas is not only a scientist but a poet as well. He arouses the curiosity and kindles the imagination."

Spurred on by this man of superior understanding, Pasteur wrote two theses, instead of one, for his doctor's degree. When the news of this degree arrived at Arbois there was great rejoicing in the Pasteur home. "We cannot judge your essays," wrote his father, "but we certainly can judge your character. You have given us nothing but satisfaction."

Indeed a satisfactory if not a brilliant career was now open to Pasteur. He received an appointment as laboratory assistant to Professor Laurent at the *École Normale*. He entered upon a series of experiments in crystallography—the study of the forms and the structures of chemical crystals—and he began to attract notice as a young man who was likely, "through sheer doggedness, to attain a fair measure of distinction."

And then suddenly he threw all his chances to the winds. The Revolution of 1848 had broken out. Pasteur's imagination took flame "at the altar of freedom." He sacrificed his savings of a hundred and fifty francs to the cause and offered, "should the occasion arise," to sacrifice his life. He left his position at the college and enlisted in the National Guard at the city of Orleans.

Fortunately the occasion for his supreme sacrifice did not arise. When the Revolution was over he returned to his laboratory and to his interrupted study of "crystalline formations in chemical substances." As a result of his painstaking researches in this field, he laid the foundation for the discovery of several new chemical compounds. "It is merely a matter of constructing new kinds of buildings," explained Pasteur, "through the chance discovery of bricks and stones cut into new shapes and sizes."

His modest "chance discovery"—actually the result of many months of assiduous research—came to the attention of M. Pouillet, professor of physics at the Sorbonne. This eminent scientist provided Pasteur with a letter of recommendation that served as an open sesame to the doors of the University of Strasbourg. "M. Pasteur," wrote Professor Pouillet, "is a most distinguished young chemist. He has just completed a remarkable series of experiments. Given the opportunity at a first class university, he should go very far . . ."

In January, 1849, Pasteur entered upon his duties as professor of chemistry at Strasbourg. And at once he set to work upon a new research—the way to a woman's heart. The young woman in question was Mlle Marie Laurent, the daughter of the rector of Strasbourg University. Shortly after his arrival at the university he wrote to the rector announcing his intention to propose to his daughter. "My father is a tanner at Arbois. My (three) sisters help him in his business and in the house, taking the place of my mother whom we have had the misfortune to lose last May. My family is comfortably off but not rich . . . As for myself, I have long ago resolved to surrender to my sisters the whole share of the inheritance which would eventually be mine. I have therefore no fortune. All that I possess is good health, good courage and my position in the University . . . I plan to devote my life to chemical research with—I hope—some degree of success . . . With these humble assets I beg to submit my suit for your daughter's hand."

The rector, like a sensible father, turned the letter over to his daughter and told her to make her own decision. The decision was unfavorable. But Pasteur was too well trained a scientist to give up a problem after a negative first result. "I am afraid," he wrote to the young lady's mother, "that Mlle Marie attaches too much importance to first impressions, which can only be unfavorable to me. There is nothing in me to attract a young girl. But memory tells me that when people have known me well, they have liked me." And like a good scientist who neglects no avenue of approach to the possible solution of his problem, he wrote a letter to Mlle Marie herself. "All that I ask of you, Mademoiselle, is not to judge me too quickly. You might be mistaken, you know. Time will show you that under this cold and shy exterior there is a heart full of affection for you."

His precise and persistent method won out. The marriage was announced for May 29, 1849. But at the last moment there was a hitch. The guests had arrived, the bride and her parents were waiting, the priest was ready for the ceremony—but there was no groom. "Where in the world is that young chemist?"

Where, but in his laboratory? His best friend, Chappuis, hurried down to the laboratory and found him there leaning over his test tubes.

"Did you forget about your wedding?"

"No."

"Then what are you doing here?"

"Finishing my work, you idiot. Surely you wouldn't expect me to quit in the middle of an experiment!"

III

His wife never regretted her decision to marry him. At times, to be sure, she scolded him for his "excessive absorption" in his work. "But I comfort her by saying that I shall lead her to fame."

And he did lead her to fame. And to sorrow. For it was not easy to be the wife of a scientist whose very brilliance aroused the jealousy and the hatred of his less gifted fellow scientists.

This jealousy and this hatred began to crop out at the very beginning of his career. His investigations had led him from chemistry to biology. "I am pursuing as best I can," he wrote to Chappuis, "the impenetrable mystery of Life and Death. I am hoping to mark a decisive step very soon by solving . . . the celebrated question of spontaneous generation." His closest friends urged him to refrain from this study. "I would advise no one," wrote Dumas, "to dwell too long on so controversial a subject."

For the origin of life was too "touchy" a question to be examined scientifically. Tradition was firmly and aggressively on the side of those who believed that life can originate spontaneously out of dead matter. Aristotle, for example, had declared that "life can be engendered by the drying of a moist body or by the moistening of a dry body." Virgil had stated that "bees can spring into life out of the carcass of a dead bull." Van Helmont had advanced the even more fantastic "method for the creation of mice" in the full-grown state: "Press a quantity of soiled linen into a vessel containing some grains of wheat or a piece of cheese for about three weeks, and at the end of this period the adult mice, both male and female, will spring up spontaneously in the vessel."

It was against this sort of traditional superstition that Pasteur dared to undertake his series of experiments. And immediately the older scientists began to aim their poisoned shafts against him. Especially virulent were Professor Pouchet, director of the Natural History Museum of Rouen, and Nicolas Joly, professor of physiology at the University of Toulouse. These two men, in order to "prove" their point against Pasteur, undertook a series of "experiments" which were neither adequately prepared nor accurately executed. "M. Pouchet and M.

Joly," wrote Pasteur to his father, "may say what they like, but truth is on my side. They do not know how to experiment. It is not an easy art; it demands, besides certain natural qualities, a long practice which naturalists have not generally acquired nowadays." But his opponents went vigorously ahead with their denunciation of Pasteur. Proclaiming to the world that they had "definitely established the fact of spontaneous generation," they called Pasteur a "circus performer, a charlatan and a clown." Pasteur bore all this contumely with a patient smile. "A man of science," he explained to his wife, "should think of what will be said of him in the coming centuries, not of the insults or the compliments of the present day."

Finally the controversy as to the probable origin of life was referred to a commission of eminent scientists, including Professor Dumas. After a thorough examination of the findings submitted by Pouchet and Joly on the one hand and by Pasteur on the other, they handed down a decision in favor of Pasteur. "Life alone can produce life."

IV

HAVING established the evidence as to the *origin* of life, Pasteur next became interested in the problem of the *preservation* of life. A mysterious disease had attacked the silkworms in the province of Alais and the entire silk business of France was threatened with ruin. Pasteur, whose achievements had now won him a seat in the Academy, was invited to investigate and if possible to check the disease. Again a tempest of abuse descended upon his head. This tempest increased in volume as month after month went by and Pasteur was able to make no headway against the epidemic. "What does a chemist know about matters of healing?" complained the mulberry cultivators whose silkworms were dying by the thousands every day. And the public took up the cry. "A chemist? Not even that. He's nothing but a parasite living on the fat of the land while the business of

France is heading for a crash." To all of which outcries and complaints Pasteur had but a single reply—"Patience."

And he needed patience. While he was investigating the silkworm epidemic one of his children died. Then another, and a third. "To go on persistently with your work under such conditions," remarked a friend, "must require a great deal of courage." "I don't know about my courage," replied Pasteur. "But I do know about my duty."

He stuck to his duty eighteen hours a day, from five in the morning to eleven at night. He suffered a paralytic stroke, and for a time the doctors despaired of his life. Yet his mind was active while his body lay paralyzed. It was in the "restful hours of his illness" that he discovered the solution to the problem upon which he had spent so much of his labor and strength. "The disease of the silkworms is inherited through diseased eggs from one generation to another. Eliminate the diseased eggs and you will produce a healthy crop of silkworms."

A simple solution after a heartbreak of toil. Yet the abuse against Pasteur did not stop even then. The silkworm seed merchants, who saw in Pasteur's formula an end to their indiscriminate selling of "bad seed for good money," began to spread malicious stories about him. As a result of these stories, the word passed around that Pasteur had utterly failed in his effort to stop the disease and that he had been driven out of Alais under a shower of stones.

When Pasteur heard this report—he was recovering from his paralysis at the time—he merely shrugged his shoulders once more. "Patience."

And his patience had its reward. The silkworm cultivators tried his remedy—and in every instance produced healthy crops. The grateful countryfolk of Alais set up a statue in his honor. But he found greater pride in "the honor of having alleviated, at my personal sacrifice, a misfortune that threatened my country."

V

His personal sacrifices had traced their story on his pale furrowed face and in his stern sad eyes. For his efforts in behalf of his fellows he received inadequate pay. Nor did he require more than he received. Once, when he visited Napoleon III and the Empress Eugénie, the imperial couple expressed their surprise at his failure to derive financial benefit from his scientific work. "In France," replied Pasteur, "a scientist would be lowering himself if he worked for personal profit." At no personal profit he undertook a series of experiments on the diseases of wine. Within a single year the French wine industry had lost several million dollars as a result of the mysterious "souring" of the produce. After a careful investigation of the matter, Pasteur discovered that this souring was due to the action of bacteria in the fermenting liquid. His problem now was to destroy the bacteria without at the same time injuring the quality of the wine. He tried several antiseptic substances, but with no result. And then he tried heating the wine to various temperatures—and came upon a tremendous discovery. If he raised the wine to a temperature of 55 degrees centigrade (about 131 degrees fahrenheit), he found that he could thus preserve the quality of the wine and at the same time destroy the poison of the bacteria.

Such was the origin of the now universally accepted process known as *pasteurization*—a process applied not only to wine but also to many other varieties of perishable foods and drinks—especially to cream and milk. If the world today enjoys a greater degree of health than was known in earlier generations, no small part of the credit is due to the patience of Pasteur in his study of the fermentation of wine.

VI

"To HELP mankind" was the primary object of his life. He entertained the hope for a day of better health, higher aspirations, and a greater understanding between man and man. "To moral coöperation through international science." But in 1870 Kaiser Wilhelm I and his chancellor of the crimson fist proclaimed a different kind of doctrine—"the glorification of force and the extinction of moral justice." And their army proceeded to put this doctrine into practice.

When the German army invaded France, Pasteur offered his services to his country, but his partial paralysis disqualified him for fighting. He showed his contempt for the German military madness, however, by returning an honorary diploma of Doctor of Medicine which he had received from the University of Bonn. "I am led by my conscience," he wrote to the Principal of the Faculty of Medicine, "to request that you efface my name from the archives of your university, and to take back that diploma, as a sign of the indignation inspired in a French scientist by the barbarity and hypocrisy of him (Kaiser Wilhelm) who, for the satisfaction of his criminal pride, persists in the massacre of two great nations." And the answer from Bonn was couched in the characteristic arrogance of the aggressor: "M. Pasteur—The undersigned, now Principal of the Faculty of Medicine of Bonn, is requested to reply to the affront which you have dared to offer to the German nation in the sacred person of its august Emperor, King Wilhelm of Prussia, by conveying to you the expression of its utter contempt . . . P.S. Wishing to keep its files free from taint, the Faculty returns your letter herewith."

With a heavy heart Pasteur noted the depredations of the invading army whose rule for conquest, as formulated by Bismarck, was "to leave the inhabitants of occupied territory nothing but their eyes to weep from."

Added to Pasteur's general distress was his personal anxiety about his son who had enlisted in the French army and who was now fighting under General Bourbaki. The news reached Pasteur that Bourbaki had sustained a disastrous defeat and that his army was fleeing before the onslaught of the Germans. The stricken old chemist and his wife started off in search of their son—hoping against hope that he might still be numbered among the living. In a dilapidated old carriage—the only vehicle available at the moment—they set out from Arbois and followed the snow-covered route of the retreating army. Everywhere the highways were littered with the bodies of the dead. Everywhere the sick and the wounded stragglers, their uniforms hanging in tatters from their frozen bodies, were begging for food and for the comfort of a blanket to wrap around their shoulders. And everywhere a desolate old man kept repeating the self-same question: "Have you seen Sergeant Pasteur?" The invariable answer was a negative shake of the head. Nobody knew whether Sergeant Pasteur was dead or alive. "All I can tell you," said one of the stragglers, "is that out of twelve hundred men in his battalion of *Chasseurs,* only three hundred are left."

Slim chance of ever meeting their son again. . . .

At last, however, there was a ray of hope. Their all but dismantled carriage had just limped into Pontarlier. A group of shivering soldiers were huddled over a fire. "Sergeant Pasteur? Yes, we saw him yesterday . . . He is still alive, but very low . . . Perhaps you can meet him on the road to Chaffois . . ."

Out of Pontarlier toward Chaffois. A cart was rumbling over the frozen road. Within it, on a bundle of straw, lay a soldier covered with a ragged coat. It was too dark to make out his features. The questing old chemist turned to the driver of the cart. "Have you seen Sergeant Pasteur?"

The soldier raised his head. "Father! Mother!" . . .

He recovered from his wounds, rejoined his regiment, and survived the war. A grain of comfort in the sorrowful life of Pasteur.

VII

AFTER the war Pasteur continued with his self-imposed task of arresting disease. In his researches on the silkworm epidemics and on the fermentations of wine he had discovered a single vital principle—that the malady in each of these cases was due to the presence of poisonous micro-organisms, or germs. Why not apply this principle in the treatment of human disease?

Pasteur was especially interested in trying out his ideas in surgery. The death rate that followed surgical operations was appalling. In the great majority of cases the decision to operate upon a patient was tantamount to a death sentence. "The opened wound," as Pasteur pointed out to a gathering at the Academy of Medicine, "is exposed to millions of germs—in the air, on the hands of the surgeon who performs the operation, in the sponges that bathe the wound, in the instruments that pry into it, and on the bandages that cover it."

When the members of the French Academy heard these words, they smiled into their beards and shook their heads and went on killing their patients with their "good old-fashioned" methods. In Scotland, however, there was one man who paid heed to Pasteur's warning. This man was Joseph Lister, professor of surgery at the University of Edinburgh. Following Pasteur's advice he submitted every object involved in the operation—his hands, his instruments, the sponges, the bandages and even the area surrounding the incision—to a thorough disinfection of carbolic acid. And with splendid results. Within two years he reduced the fatalities of his surgical cases from ninety per cent to fifteen per cent.

Yet the surgeons of the French Academy remained stubbornly opposed to Pasteur's theory of disinfection, even in the face of Lister's successful application of this theory. It was a new idea and therefore—they argued—it was a *bad* idea.

As for Pasteur, he was ready to accept and to fight for any idea—especially in the field of medicine—as soon as it was definitely supported by adequate facts. "The facts with regard to surgery have demonstrated, beyond the shadow of a doubt, that many a patient has died through the poisonous action of the Infinitesimally Small." And so he entered upon a crusade to stamp out a double source of infection—the physical microbe that attacked the human body, and the "mental microbe" that retarded the human mind. "I will force them to see in spite of themselves," he said again and again of his opponents. "They *must* see!" One day a member of the Academy of Medicine was lecturing to his colleagues on puerperal (childbirth) fever—a disease which in 1864 had killed over three hundred women in the Paris Maternity Hospital alone. The lecturer was explaining his ideas as to the cause of this fever, when a voice interrupted him: "Nonsense and fiddlesticks! It isn't any of the things you mention, but the doctors and the nurses that are responsible for puerperal fever. They murder the mothers by carrying the microbe from an infected patient to a healthy one!"

"And can you tell me," asked the lecturer sarcastically, "what this microbe of yours looks like?"

Whereupon Pasteur walked to the blackboard, took a piece of chalk and rapidly sketched the outline of a chain-like organism. "There, that is what it looks like."

The meeting was thrown into an uproar. The older doctors insisted that Pasteur was an interloper, an amateur, a man who knew nothing whatsoever about medicine and who had better stick to his chemicals and his crucibles. The younger men, however, paid heed to his words. Little by little they introduced his methods of sterilization until, as one of Pasteur's biographers (L. Descours) remarks, "the maternity hospitals ceased to be the ante-chambers of death."

VIII

PASTEUR continued to befuddle the reactionaries, to bring down their denunciations upon his head, and to fight his scientific battles for the preservation of life. Through his methodical process of repeated experimentation he discovered the principle of immunizing a person against the *violent* form of a disease by inoculating him with a *mild* form of that disease. This simple method of transforming a virus into a vaccine has saved an incalculable number of lives.

He first employed this discovery in the stamping out of an epidemic of anthrax—a deadly fever of the spleen—that threatened to exterminate the sheep and cattle industry of France. In the course of his researches in this field he was obliged, as usual, to fight not only against the virulence of the plague but against the equally stubborn virulence of human prejudice. At one of the meetings of the Academy of Medicine, Pasteur accused his adversaries of malignity as well as of stupidity. Whereupon one of the physicians, Dr Jules Guérin, started up from his chair and made a rush at Pasteur. The pugnacious doctor was held back by a fellow member of the Academy, but the meeting ended in a general uproar.

The next day Guérin challenged Pasteur to a duel. But Pasteur returned the challenge. "My business," he said, "is to heal, not to kill."

And then came the most dramatic episode in his lifelong business of healing—his famous battle against hydrophobia. For some years he had been experimenting with the inoculation of the saliva of mad dogs into healthy rabbits. At times he varied his experiments by subjecting the rabbits directly to the bites of the mad dogs. On one occasion a large bulldog, though furious with pain and foaming at the mouth, persistently refused to bite the rabbit that had been thrust into his cage. It would be necessary, concluded Pasteur, to *suck* the saliva out of the dog's jaws and then to inject it into the rabbit.

The dog was tied securely upon a table and Pasteur, with a glass tube in his mouth, bent down to the mouth of the enraged animal. "This," wrote a bystander, "was the supreme moment of Pasteur's life." Calmly, as if unaware of the fact that he was courting death, he sucked the venomous saliva drop by drop into the tube. And then, when he had gathered a sufficient quantity of the poison into the tube, he turned to his assistants. "Well, gentlemen, we can now proceed with the experiment."

Within a few months after this experiment an Alsatian boy, Joseph Meister, was bitten by a mad dog. His mother, on the advice of the local physician, took him to Pasteur. Here was an opportunity to test out on a human being the anti-rabic inoculation that had proved so successful in the case of animals.

Yet Pasteur hesitated. How certain could he feel that his remedy would succeed? Was it not within the realm of possibility that the inoculation, instead of preserving the victim's life, would only introduce a more aggravated type of the disease? Was he therefore justified in taking the risk, especially when it concerned another person's life?

He took the risk. And he won. The night following the final inoculation was one of sleepless terror for Pasteur but of peaceful sleep for the stricken child. Thirty-one days passed, and there were no recurring symptoms of the disease. The boy was completely cured. Pasteur had conquered hydrophobia.

IX

A NUMBER of belated distinctions—election to the Academy, the Cross of the Legion of Honor, medals, ribbons, diplomas, banquets, ovations, parades—and Pasteur remained through it all a modest seeker for truth. His present popularity was as amazing to him as his earlier disgrace. "I can't understand why people make such a fuss over me." Elected by the Government to represent his country at the International Medical Congress in London, he entered St James's Hall amidst a thunder of cheers. Unaware that he was the cause of the acclamation, he turned to his escort. "It must be the Prince of Wales arriving. I'm sorry I didn't come earlier."

He returned to Paris and to his work at the Pasteur Institute—a hospital built in his honor for the combating of infectious disease. And here he spent the rest of his days in his "humble effort," as he expressed it, "to extend the frontiers of life."

His seventieth birthday was the occasion of a national holiday. Pasteur attended a celebration in his honor at the Sorbonne. He was too feeble, however, to express in person his thanks to the delegates who had come from various countries to join in the celebration. He asked his son to read his speech for him. "Gentlemen . . . you bring me the greatest happiness that can be experienced by a man whose invincible belief is that science and peace will triumph over ignorance and war . . . Never permit the sadness of certain hours which pass over nations to discourage you . . . Have faith that in the long run the nations will learn to unite not for destruction but for coöperation, and that the future will belong not to the conquerors but the saviors of mankind . . ."

This was Pasteur's farewell message to the world.

KELVIN

Great Scientific Contributions by Kelvin

Experiments in the measurement of the atom, heat, refrigeration, electricity, etc.

INVENTIONS:
Siphon recorder.
Galvanometer.
New type of compass, etc.

BOOKS AND TREATISES:
On Natural Philosophy.
On Electricity and Magnetism.
Mathematical Papers.
Popular Lectures and Addresses (3 volumes).
The Wave Theory of Light.
The Molecular Tactics of a Crystal.
The Dynamic Theory of Heat.

Kelvin

Lord Kelvin
(William Thomson)
1824–1907

HE CAME of a race of Scotch Covenanters who had been persecuted out of their country for their religion. At the age of twelve he lost his mother. His father, a professor of natural philosophy at Glasgow University, provided for his six children a system of education that would toughen their minds for the protection of their hearts. He planned this system of education to be wide as well as deep. Almost from infancy the children grew up with a friendship for extended vistas of thought. They absorbed the principles of geology and of astronomy. Plants were their playmates. They learned about the struggles of empires to gain new victories and about the struggles of ideas to win a foothold among men. Around the table they peered with fascination at the toy globe of the earth and took dream trips to its furthermost limits. And then they transferred their gaze to another and vaster globe that their father had bought for them— the sphere of the heavens with its epic story of which the earth was merely a syllable.

William was the youngest of the children, but he had the keenest imagination of them all. He found himself spellbound by this tale of the two globes. At an early age he had accepted the challenge to unravel the mystery of its plot. When he was sixteen years old he transcribed in his diary an eleventh commandment—an intellectual call to his reason just as the Ten Commandments were a religious call to his conscience:

> *Mount where Science guides:*
> *Go, measure earth, weigh air, and state the tides;*
> *Instruct the planets in what orbs to run,*
> *Correct old Time and regulate the sun.*

II

His RISE to intellectual maturity was rapid. At seventeen he entered the University of Cambridge. At eighteen he wrote an outstanding paper on the dynamics of heat and contributed several articles to the *Cambridge Mathematical Journal.* Upon graduation he met some of the leading physicists of France and of England and gave them valuable suggestions on their researches. At twenty-two he was appointed professor at the University of Glasgow.

His aggressive vitality was rather too much for the mild-mannered Scots who served as his colleagues on the faculty. Hardly had he been elected to an honor coveted by many a gray-haired rival when he determined to revolutionize the department of physics at Glasgow. He came to his elders with a request for a room where he might carry on his experiments outside of his classes. It was an unheard-of piece of audacity. For generations the economical Scottish professors had been content to mess up their lecture halls with their experiments. Why in the world should this young upstart require a special room all by himself?

Yet their curiosity got the better of their resentment. "If you insist upon it, you can have the old cellar from which we'll remove the wine barrels."

And thus the first modern laboratory in the British Isles was born in a wine cellar.

Young Thomson set to work with the gusto of a hurricane.

He was the perfect personification of his own theory of dynamics. Organizing a staff of thirty volunteers from his class of ninety students, he kept them going at a furious pace. The work piled up so rapidly that he found he needed more space—"an extra room for thinking."

Again his colleagues looked at him in amazement. "You may occupy the tower," they said.

From morning to night he plumbed the depths and scaled the heights. From experimental activity to abstract speculation. And in the evening he walked to his home—only fifty yards away—where the body of the technician and the soul of the philosopher resigned themselves to the sleep of a man in perfect health.

III

AGAIN the dynamite of his energy exploded amidst the conservatism of his colleagues. He demanded still more space. And again they acceded to his demand. "Professor Thomson, you have a marvelous genius for annexation."

The academic and the lay world alike were mystified at the outpouring of his enthusiasm. For a period of weeks the visitors who came to the laboratory to watch him at his work were startled to find him blowing soap bubbles. And all the students in the room walked back and forth for hours with their faces puffed and their eyes shining as they kept releasing bubble after bubble into the air. One of the visitors ventured to ask for the meaning of all this activity.

The professor glared at him for a few seconds. And then in a tone that implied pity for anyone who was unable to draw his own conclusions from such obvious evidence, he replied: "I am calculating the thickness of the uncolored spot on the soap bubble. I have found that this thickness measures one twenty-millionth of a millimeter." The following month he confided to another visitor that he had ordered his students to smoke their pipes and to blow rings from their lips in order to illustrate the dynamical model of the atom. "I have measured the atom, too," he explained. "I have found it to be one two-hundred-millionth of a centimeter in size."

He was exciting to the students, this mercurial professor of theirs. One never knew what he was going to do next. One day his friend Helmholtz, the German scientist, came to the laboratory and watched his experiment with a gyroscope. A heavy metal top was spinning rapidly. The professor wanted to show that the top would become rigid in its rotation and hoped thus by analogy to prove the rigidity of the earth. Suddenly he seized a hammer and hit the top a crashing blow. The metal flew off in a centrifugal direction and crashed through Helmholtz's hat which was hanging on a rack. The students were in an uproar. Helmholtz joined feebly in the laughter. "Something went wrong," explained the professor innocently. "I'll buy you a new hat."

There was nothing dull about his teaching. "I've put an end to the reading of stale essays," he said. His classroom and his research laboratory were packed with all sorts of apparatus. Nothing was left to the imagination. Gadgets were heaped upon tables; they hung from the ceilings; they were fastened to the walls. Triple spiral spring vibrators, a pendulum thirty feet long with a twelve pound cannon ball suspended from the end, a terrifying machine in which a number of billiard balls kept speeding hither and thither to illustrate the dynamics of a nebula, heaps upon heaps of gyroscopes. He whirled one on top of the other, he twisted and tortured and juggled them in his efforts to study the gyrations of the planets. In one corner, suspended from the ceiling, was an innocent-looking device—a metal ring covered with rubber "to illustrate the nature of the dewfall." One day he called for water and poured it upon the ring until the rubber bulged downward. More water. Finally the rubber burst "like an overburdened dewdrop"—right over the heads of the students sitting in the front row. "I always like my illustrations to soak in," chuckled the professor.

[222]

His "lectures" were not lectures at all in the usual sense. They were feats of mental—and of physical—gymnastics. "He sprang like a tiger into the classroom," observed one of his students, "tearing off his professor's gown as he bounded down the aisle to the platform." He hurried through the prescribed text in the Bible and then looked smilingly at the students. "Today I will lecture on the propagation of luminar motion through a turbulently moving inviscid liquid."

They hardly understood a word of what he said. But they were fascinated by his gestures. When he talked about the dance of the stars, he was as likely as not to execute a jig upon the platform. A solemn algebraic formula—and then presto. He would reach for the pointer and balance it on top of his finger while a hundred men held their breath. "See here. If I balanced this pointer upon a granite mountain, it would strain the entire earth." When he lectured on the principles of sound he produced an old French horn that he had played in the orchestra during his college days and blew upon it a mighty musical blast as the students rose to their feet and cheered. If he spoke on the principles of velocity, he took out an old rifle that he had once carried as a guardsman and fired a volley of shots at the pendulum.

Like all other men of vigorous personality, he had his prejudices. He was particularly incensed against the "muddled human system of weights and measures." And for good reason. Once, while preparing to shoot at the pendulum, he had instructed his assistant to load the rifle with a "dram" of powder. He was referring to the avoirdupois dram. But the assistant thought he wanted the apothecaries' dram, which is twice the amount of the avoirdupois unit. Accordingly he put into the rifle a sufficient charge of powder to have blown off the professor's head—and the heads of a few of his star pupils as well. Happily the marksman, just as he was about to fire, discovered the error. "I have always been suspicious of the words and the works of the human mind," the professor sighed.

IV

As FOR HIMSELF, he was a man of precise words and of practical works. He took a greater interest in concrete mechanical devices than he did in abstract mechanical laws. He had assumed the active directorship of a factory in addition to what he called his "passive" professorial duties. When the French physicist, Joule, had announced his startling theory that heat was an energy which could be transformed into work he immediately seized upon the practical application of this theory and busied himself with plans to harness the energy for industrial use. He devoted a great deal of thought to the concept that was making its way into the physics of the mid-century—the idea of energy as the source of matter. From his study in thermodynamics he caught a glimpse of the mighty principle of the transformation and the indestructibility of energy—and this eminently practical man who thought of all knowledge in terms of its "usefulness" to humanity, found himself paradoxically enough embarking upon a theoretical philosophy of life. "Every planet," he explained to his pupils, "is like a toe dancer. It is poised and balanced. It is all aquiver with living energy." But what was the *nature* of this energy? At fifty-three he began to write a book on the subject. But he never completed it, for he could find no answer to his question.

His study of thermodynamics—the energizing power of heat— ranged all the way from the outermost limits of the universe to the confines of his own person. He wore a woolen vest as a sort of thermostat to regulate the temperature of his body. Whenever he felt cold he would pile on several more vests; whenever he felt warm he would discard them. In the winter it was nothing for him to wear eight or nine of these vests. To his friends who laughed at this idiosyncrasy he declared haughtily: "To every man his proper vest, to suit his time and temper best." Life was all a matter of temperature.

He constantly observed his surroundings with a view to improving them—not only for himself but for the general public as well. One day he looked at his supper with a sudden inspiration. Why not apply his studies of the human body to the heating and the cooling of food? At high temperatures the molecules of matter are extremely active. At low temperatures they are extremely sluggish. Heat hastens the process of change; cold retards it. Across the channel, in France, Pasteur had demonstrated the fact that germs could be destroyed at very high temperatures and that foods could be preserved by a process of boiling. Here in England it dawned on Thomson that germs might also be destroyed at very low temperatures and that food could thus be preserved by the process of cooling! Such was the paradoxical practicality of William Thomson's mind.

As he walked over the fields early in the morning he observed how the dew had helped to protect the vegetation from the frosts of the night. And in this simple protective process he beheld the principle of one of the most modern of the arts—refrigeration. Thus two contemporary scientists were almost simultaneously harnessing the heat and the cold for the better health of mankind. The future generations were to subsist largely upon a diet of pasteurized liquids and kelvinized solids.

But the English physicist was more fortunate than the French chemist. While the Frenchmen hounded Pasteur almost into the grave the Englishmen raised Thomson to a peerage.

And so "Wullie Tamson"—as his Scottish friends still called him—became the first Baron Kelvin. The king took him into his council, and people bowed and scraped before him. But "Wullie Tamson" remained the same honest, energetic, outspoken, playful child of a man. It was with a childish delight that he once heard himself announced at a dinner party on the occasion of his visit to America. Unexpectedly detained on important business, he had been late in arriving at his friend's house. Six-thirty, seven, seven-thirty—and still no sign of Lord Kelvin. Everybody was alarmed when suddenly the draperies were parted and the colored butler announced with a booming voice: "Ladies and gen'lmen, de Lawd am come!"

It was as a judge of the scientific section at the Centennial Exposition in Philadelphia that Lord Kelvin had been invited to America. He spent six weeks examining every mechanical device on the exhibition grounds. Finally, as he was getting ready to depart, a friend asked him to look at a "funny little contraption" lying on a table in an out-of-the-way corner. Kelvin walked over to the table. Several of the judges were making sarcastic remarks about the "contraption" as the inventor tried to explain its use. Kelvin picked up the instrument and looked at it. At this moment a pompous individual walked up to the table. It was Dom Pedro, the emperor of Brazil. He held out his hand to the inventor. "Professor Bell, I am delighted to see you again."

"Thank you, Your Majesty."

"Tell me, have you made any further progress with your telephone?"

"If it please Your Majesty, pick it up and listen. I shall go to the other end of the room and say a few words."

Alexander Graham Bell walked to the end of the wire. Dom Pedro took the instrument in his hand. "My God, it talks!"

"Do you mind if I try it?" It was Lord Kelvin speaking. Then, as he put the instrument to his ear—"It certainly does talk! It's the most amazing thing I've seen in America!"

And he returned to England determined to put this "most amazing" of inventions before the British public. He encountered a torrent of abuse from every newspaper and magazine in the country. "The inventor of the so-called telephone is an impostor —a ventriloquist—a fraud." The *London Times* devoted a column to the "scientific" explanation of the reasons why the human voice could never be sent along an electric wire. But Kelvin persisted. And finally he got the British public to listen to the new voice.

V

HIS UNFLAGGING ENERGY prompted him to take an active part in every scientific endeavor. Having interested himself in Faraday's magnetic and electric researches, he had found an opportunity to translate his predecessor's theories into practical use. He had been appointed technical advisor to the company organized by Sir Charles Bright and Cyrus Field for the purpose of laying the Atlantic cable between England and America. It was Kelvin's perfection of the galvanometer—or needle detector—which "picked up" the almost imperceptible current of electricity that trickled out from the cable after a trip of over two thousand miles. And it was Kelvin's invention of the siphon recorder—or electric pen—which finally "wrote out" the cabled message in a wavy line upon a piece of paper.

A wavy line upon a piece of paper—nothing more. Kelvin was a hard-headed scientist. He laughed at the effusions of the poets who rhapsodized about the "miracles" of his inventions. He saw life as an essay in logic and not as a work of art. One day his friends took him to hear a Beethoven symphony. He was greatly impressed. He reached for his little notebook with its green covers—he had filled hundreds of them with his observations. "Think what a complicated thing is the result of an orchestra playing," he wrote. "Think of the smooth gradual increase and diminution of pressure . . . A single curve, drawn in the manner of the curve of the price of cotton, describes all that the ear can possibly hear . . ."

Lines and curves and angles of energetic power—such was the world concept of this tough-minded man of science. Tough-minded and gentle-hearted. For seventeen years he took care of an invalid wife. Every morning he carried her down to the parlor and every evening he carried her up to bed. And when she died, he was for a time inconsolable.

But nature smites with one hand and caresses with the other.

Three years after the loss of his wife he found another woman. It was a strictly scientific courtship. He had met her at Madeira while he was superintending the construction of a cable from England to Brazil. He taught her the art of telegraphy. For sixteen days they exchanged innumerable dots and dashes of love— he from the ship where they were repairing the cable, she from her villa on the shore. Finally, as the ship was steaming away, he signaled to her in the code they understood so well: "I will come back for you." And she signaled in reply: "I will wait."

VI

As he grew older, he complained that the time was passing too rapidly for him. "A second is too short; we must have longer units." Every day he spent several hours dictating. A secretary on one side of him, a secretary on the other, each taking down notes on an entirely different subject. Hustle, hustle, hustle! The years are fleeting! "Those who live slowly create their own obstacles." He had planned enough work for two centuries and his problem was to "finish it in a single lifetime." Always he gave orders, always he expressed opinions, always he "dissected" ideas —until his parrot, Dr Hookbeak, shouted shrilly at him from her cage: "Lord Kelvin! Lord Kelvin! Shut up!"

And now he was nearing the end of the road. A lifetime of theories and inventions, only to be swept into the shadow by newer theories and better inventions. William Roentgen, Henri Becquerel, Pierre and Marie Curie—what a vast rich field they had opened up for future investigation! What a revolution they had produced in the scientific conception of the world! How inadequate was his own conception as compared to theirs! He smiled ironically on the occasion of the fiftieth anniversary of his assumption of the professorship at Glasgow. His friends were enumerating the achievements of his career—the new compass that was impervious to the oscillations of gunfire, the sounding wire that warned sailors against hidden rocks, the machine that enabled men to forecast the tides, the instrument that registered the strength of an electric current passing through a wire, dozens of practical devices for the more accurate recordings of weights and measures, and so on and on. Mere toys for children. "I am not really an inventor. I am just a dreamer sleeping in the arms of the past."

Three years after his jubilee he resigned his professorship at the University of Glasgow. The trustees informed him that they would have been glad to retain his services, but he shook his head. "No sentimentality, if you please. I have outlived my usefulness."

He faced his students for the last time. "It has come to be my belief that as a man grows older, the pictures he looks upon with the most pleasure by his fireside are those which bring before him again his college days. . . . Make your whole life full of pictures which are bright, and clear, and clean."

And so he left his professorship. But not the university. As long as there was breath in his body he could never break the last tie with old Glasgow. At the beginning of the academic year of 1899 this aged scholar of seventy-six walked into the registration room along with the undergraduates and enrolled his name —"Lord Kelvin, Research Student." He was at last too wise to teach. From now on he would only learn.

And then the sagest of teachers, Death, sought out this student in his eighty-third year and led him forward to the Great Laboratory for his Final Experiment.

HAECKEL

Haeckel

PROPERTY OF
CARNEGIE INSTITUTE OF TECHNOLOGY
LIBRARY

Ernst Heinrich Haeckel

1834–1919

"IN A RECENT microscopical lecture," wrote Haeckel to his parents during his college days at Würzburg, "Professor Leydig suddenly stopped and pointed to me with the greatest astonishment. 'I've never seen the like of it in my life!' he cried. 'This young man can look through the microscope with the left eye while with the right eye he can draw what he sees . . .' This curiosity in my physical make-up," continued Haeckel, "is of the utmost importance in the study of natural history."

Together with his double physical vision Haeckel was blessed with a double mental vision. One half of him was an observant scientist; the other half, an imaginative artist. He was equally adept at sketching a human muscle and at painting a rural landscape. It was this combination of the seeing eye and the aspiring heart that made him one of the outstanding German personalities of the nineteenth century.

II

HIS STOCK was a mixture of nobility and peasantry—with the peasant element in the ascendant. He never to the end of his days acquired the refined artificialities of the aristocracy. In his youth he describes himself as "a wild lad with chubby red cheeks and long blond hair . . . careless in my dress and frequently forgetful of my table manners." Shy in the presence of other people, he was passionately fond of walking, swimming and collecting all sorts of curious plants. Always on his holidays from school he went off adventuring into the forest in quest of "new specimens of growing and living things." When his elders asked him what he wanted to become he answered, "I will be a *Reiser*"—a childish form of the word *Reisender,* a traveler.

He was destined, however, to do most of his traveling on the mental rather than on the physical plane. His father, a government official, moved his family from Potsdam to Merseburg and from Merseburg to Berlin. But Ernst did not accompany his parents to Berlin. Instead, he matriculated at the University of Würzburg. Here he hoped to specialize in botany with a view to following "the footsteps of Humboldt and Darwin into the tropical forests." His parents, however, had other hopes for him. They wanted him to specialize in medicine.

His entire university career was a struggle between his distaste for medicine and his passion for botany. "I am convinced," he wrote again and again to his parents, "that medicine is not my field." . . . "The study of disease fills me with an unconquerable disgust (which is due probably to weak nerves and hypochondria) and I shall never be able to adapt myself to it." On the other hand, he experienced the keenest delight whenever he discovered a new plant. "The day before yesterday I took a walk on the shore near the Main where the ships unload their cargoes. Suddenly I found among the shrubbery a strange, yellow-colored, cruciferous plant, related to the *black cabbage* but still quite unknown to me . . . Can you imagine my ecstasy!"

But his parents couldn't imagine his ecstasy. They told him to forget about his plants and to stick to his medicine. And Haeckel dutifully complied with their wishes. He bought a microscope—having saved up the money for it by subsisting for a

time on "sour kidney and buttermilk soup"—and plunged faithfully into his anatomical studies. He successfully completed these
studies and absorbed his *materia medica*—"the most terrible instrument of torture ever devised for the intellect of man"—and
passed his examinations for the doctor's degree. "And now, my
dear parents, here I am—Herr Doktor Haeckel—a lanky,
dried-up lath of a young medico, with shaggy, yellow-brown hair,
a mustache and a beard—only three or four inches long—of the
same color, and with a long pipe in his mouth." But when he
comes home, Haeckel warns his parents, he will bring along with
him something besides his microscope and his medical books.
"You will have to reserve an extra room for a beautiful haycock
(of plant specimens). This will become a pleasant addition to
my botanical treasure house."

Even though he was now licensed to practice medicine, he
looked upon "the hit-or-miss art of healing" as a high class form
of quackery. "When you get sick," he said, "you can choose one
of two courses. You can leave it to nature if you want to recover, or you can go to a doctor if you want to die."

Nevertheless he was "reconciled," as he told his parents, "to
the thought of a medical career." For several weeks he served as
an interne at the Würzburg Hospital, attending to the births of
"those rascally babies who insist upon coming into the world at
an hour when all honest people ought to be sound asleep." His
"obstetrical duties" came at a most inopportune time—precisely
nine months after the Würzburg Carnival. "During the period
of my service at the lying-in hospital the babies arrived literally in
shoals, so that I was awakened several nights in succession."

And yet, "since medicine is to be my career, I will try my
best to endure it." Indeed, with the scientific nonchalance of the
"finished" medical student he began to look forward to his
first post mortem—"the most interesting, yea the *only* interesting
part of medicine." And then he got his initial post mortem—
an autopsy upon the body of a fellow interne "to whom I had

been talking intimately only a few days ago." This episode cured him of his medical ambitions for the rest of his life.

In deference to the wishes of his parents, however, he continued his medical practice for one year. But during this entire period he had only three patients—owing principally to the fact that he fixed his consultation hour from five to six in the morning. By the end of the year he had succeeded in proving to his father that he was not "cut out" for the medical profession.

What to do now? Unfit for medicine in spite of his training, he felt equally unfit for botany because of the *inadequacy* of his training. For a time he played with the idea of devoting his life to landscape painting. But he realized that as an artist he was merely a gifted imitator and not a creative genius. Good enough for an amateur—he painted in his lifetime more than a thousand landscapes—but woefully incompetent (he confessed to himself) for a professional.

And so at twenty-five he found himself confronted with a dark wall. Yet somewhere, he believed, an opening would rise unexpectedly out of this impenetrable darkness. For he had an eager faith in God—this young man who later was to deny His existence. In a letter to his parents he expressed his determination, under the guidance of heaven, to face the future unperturbed: "Fear God, do that which is right, and be afraid of no man."

III

JUST AS HE HAD EXPECTED he found his opportunity—or rather, he *seized* his opportunity—in the field of natural science. He had wheedled his father into allowing him a year's vacation "for travel and general study." He spent the greater part of the year in fishing for "rare forms of sea life" at Messina. Among other interesting specimens he discovered and studied and classified those "pure and beautiful snowflakes of the sea"—the *radiolaria*. He prepared a monograph on this subject and on the strength of it secured a professorship in zoölogy at the University of Jena.

And then came the first of his two tragic romances. He fell in love with his cousin, Anna Sethe, a young woman "of rare gifts of mind and soul." They were married and lived happily—for just two years. It was precisely on his thirtieth birthday that his young wife died.

For a time his friends feared that he wouldn't survive the blow. "Work alone can save me from going mad." And so he plunged into his work and prepared within a single year a twelve-hundred-page summary of his scientific ideas—the *General Morphology of Organisms*. Throughout the writing of this manuscript Haeckel lived like a hermit, working eighteen hours a day and getting about three or four hours' sleep out of the twenty-four.

Haeckel dedicated this book as a living monument to his wife. He named after her one of his favorite *medusae*—a fairy-like jellyfish "whose long, trailing tentacles remind me of her lovely golden hair."

Three years later he married again—this time not out of love but out of a desire for companionship. He moved into a "roomy" cottage which he named the *Villa Medusa* and settled down to a lifelong study of the mystery of life. For exercise he took long walks—he was always a good athlete, having established a record in the broad jump—puttered around in his garden, and pounded on his chest with his fists "to make it breathe deeply" as he stood at the open window of his bedroom. Sometimes he resorted to this chest-pounding on his way from his house to the college—to the great amusement of his students.

In the lecture-room, however, his students felt nothing but the highest admiration for their teacher who "talked like the devil and sketched like a god." Sitting at a small table, except when he got up to draw a diagram on the blackboard, he delivered his lectures in a voice that was "perfervid, scintillating, assured." He expressed his ideas with deference to few and with apologies to none. He suffered from no sense of false modesty. One day when a friend asked him, "Who is your favorite author?" he promptly replied, "Ernst Haeckel."

But if his favorite author was Ernst Haeckel, his favorite scientist was Charles Darwin.

IV

IT WAS IN 1866 that Haeckel met "the genealogist of the world's greatest family tree." This meeting with Darwin, Haeckel tells us, was one of the supreme moments of his life. "The carriage stopped before Darwin's pleasant ivy-covered and elm-shaded country house. Then, emerging from amidst the creepers which surrounded the shadowy porch, I saw the great scientist advancing towards me—a tall and venerable figure, with the broad shoulders of an atlas supporting a world of thought . . . The charming, candid expression of the whole face, the soft, gentle voice, the slow, deliberate speech, the simple and natural train of his ideas, took my whole heart captive during the first hour of our conversation, just as his sublime words had taken my whole mind by storm at the first reading. It was as if some exalted sage of Hellenic antiquity, some Socrates or Aristotle, stood in the flesh before me."

Haeckel became the champion of Darwin in Germany just as Huxley had become his champion in England. ("The heresy of Darwinism," remarked an English clergyman, "has now entered upon an unholy alliance of three H's—Haeckel, Huxley and Hell.") Unlike Darwin, Haeckel announced himself aggressively as a missionary of free thought. "There is no God," he said. "And," added a facetious adversary, "Haeckel is His prophet." He attacked the "fanaticism of religion" with an equally vehement fanaticism of irreligion. He wrote book after book to disprove the divinity of God and to establish the divinity of Nature. And with the appearance of each book a new avalanche of vituperation fell upon the head of the author.

At the turn of the century, when evolution had become somewhat respectable, a visitor at the University of Jena spoke to the janitor about the popularity of Haeckel's courses. "Yes," replied the janitor, "but I have seen him stoned down that street there." When he delivered one of his early lectures on Darwinism to a great assembly of naturalists, the audience rose in a body and left him to expound his ideas to an empty room. On another occasion when he came as a delegate to a Freethinkers' Convention at Rome, the Pope ordered a "divine fumigation" of the entire city.

The name of Haeckel was anathema everywhere—except in the little University of Jena. Here he remained undisturbed for fifty years. More than once he offered to resign from the university in order that "it may escape the stigma of harboring an infidel." But Dr Seebeck, the head of the governing body, always refused his offer. "I don't like your ideas, and that is why I insist upon your remaining here. In a little university you have but a little influence. In a bigger university, however, you can do a great deal of harm . . . Besides, the older you get, the less radical you'll become."

And Haeckel grew older and became *more* radical—and still remained at Jena. As time went on and his ideas became popular, he received numerous offers from larger universities at more attractive salaries. But he turned them all down. Here at Jena Goethe had written some of his finest lyrics. Here Schiller had taught history for ten years. Haeckel loved the traditions of the college. And he loved the atmosphere of the town—*das liebe närrische Nest,* with its meandering cobble-stoned streets, its Gothic towers, its fragrant little gardens and its gossipy houses whose gables, like the faces of beldames in fluted red caps, leaned toward one another "in a perpetual whisper." Above all, he loved the Thuringian Mountains that ringed the little city and kept away from it the noises and the traffic of the outside world. "Here I have everything I want, everything I can use. Why should I think of uprooting my life?"

[239]

In this quiet fruit-bowl of a valley nestled under the inverted bowl of the heavens he took his long walks and delivered his lectures and wrote his books and formulated the outlines of a new scientific credo—"the irreligious religion of *Monism*."

V

THE *Monism* of Haeckel is the *Pantheism* of Spinoza translated into the scientific language of the nineteenth century. *Monism* (from the Greek *monos*, which means *single* or *alone*) is the doctrine that the entire universe is a single unit. This doctrine is opposed to the *Dualistic* theory that the universe consists of two parts—the *Creator* of the World and the *Created* World.

The world, according to Haeckel, has not been created by an external God. It is the result of "one great process of evolution operating through an unbroken chain of transformations that are causally connected."

In this causal and unbroken chain of connections all plants and animals form a single genealogical tree from the primordial cell to the modern man.

The soul of man is no different from the soul of the lower animals. Both in men and in animals the soul is nothing more than "the totality of the cerebral functions." These living functions of the brain are ended at death, and so it is absurd—declares Haeckel—"to believe in the personal immortality of the soul."

Just as there is no soul distinct from the body of man, so too there is no God distinct from the body of the world. God is the sum total of the matter and the energy—the body and the spirit—that compose the inseparable unit of the world's substance.

So much for the theoretical side of Monism. Let us now take a brief glance at the practical side. In the evolutionary struggle for existence—asserts Haeckel—the law of competition among the lower animals gives way to the law of coöperation among men. The human individual can best survive through the application of the social instinct of reciprocal interdependence. The most effective form of government for human society is *Nomocracy*—the rule of justice in accordance with the laws of nature. These laws of nature, as applied to human conduct, require mutual respect for one another's opinions, tolerance in religious matters, and freedom for the individual up to but not beyond the point where his freedom would interfere with the freedom of other individuals.

This scientific approach to human ethics brings Haeckel—and he admits it—very close to the religious approach. In summarizing the "rational morality" of his monistic religion he concludes that "man, since he is a gregarious (social) animal, must strive to attain the natural equilibrium between his two different obligations—the behest of egoism and the behest of altruism. The ethical principle of the *Golden Rule* has expressed this double obligation twenty-five hundred years ago in the maxim: *Do unto others as you would that they should do unto you.*"

And thus we find in Haeckel the paradox of a man who denies God and accepts Jesus. After all, Haeckel was not a *freethinker* but a *free thinker*. Released from the shackles of prejudice he had chosen a new path to the heart of the world's mystery. And he had found there the selfsame truth that had been discovered by the prophets of the old religions. The old prophets had said, "God is love." Haeckel merely paraphrased these words into the scientific dictum, "Nature is friendly toward the noblest aspirations of man."

VI

AT THE AGE OF SIXTY-FIVE he put all his scientific and philosophic thought into a single volume—*The Riddle of the Universe*. It became an immediate best seller and remained so for a quarter of a century. But he derived little joy from his success. For in the course of the writing of this book he had entered upon the second of his tragic romances. One day in 1898 he received a letter from an unknown young woman. "Please forgive this intrusion from a stranger, and be a little patient. I will write as briefly as a woman can . . . By accident one of your books, *The Natural History of Creation,* fell into my hands. What a new world rose before me! . . . Is it any wonder that I require more after having read your book? . . . Will you reach me your hand, my esteemed Professor, and tell me what to read? . . ." Signed, *Franziska von Altenhausen.*

Haeckel sent her a list of books to read. After a few more letters they exchanged pictures, and then they exchanged hearts. Haeckel was unhappy at the Villa Medusa. His life had been embittered by the incessant nagging of a feeble-minded daughter and an invalid wife. Here was a young woman—she was only thirty—who soothed his "wounded old heart" with the balm of adoration. For five years they kept up a clandestine and passionate correspondence. "What an amazing thing"—he wrote—"that a young girl like you and an old man like me should have fallen so desperately in love with each other!" And Franziska wrote back: "Don't call yourself an old man. In spirit you are a young god."

They had several secret trysts, in various parts of Germany. "From the depths of my heart," he wrote to her after their first meeting, "I thank you for the two memorable days that brought me the happiness of your personal acquaintance . . . You must surely have perceived from my awkward behavior how completely your kind visit has upset the ordinary composure of my prosaic existence—the radiance of a sweet spring fairy who brings fragrant blossoms to the dungeon of a poor, lonely captive."

After another meeting—"How enchanting was our bridal journey yesterday!"

And Franziska to Haeckel, after still another meeting—"Our

dear days together seemed to me like a beautiful dream too lovely to endure. Its memory still enfolds me so magically that it is difficult for me to express in words what moves my heart. Only be sure of this—in those few hours you grew far, far dearer to me than ever before."

Age, wrote Haeckel in one of his letters to Franziska, is no guard against folly. Torn between his disloyalty toward his own wife—he deceived her, he said, for her own peace of mind—and his infatuation for Franziska, he entertained for a time the idea of committing suicide. "The important question of self-destruction (the very term is nonsense—it should be called self-deliverance) has occurred to me very often in recent weeks." He gave up this thought in favor of another avenue of escape—a trip to the Indian Ocean. "Franziska, dearest, best beloved wife of my heart—I depart for the tropical seas to escape from you and from myself—two rare and extraordinary souls made for each other—who, separated, must wander lonely through life . . ." He traveled to India, Singapore, Buitenzorg, Sumatra, Java—but wherever he went he carried along his sorrow. "Man," he wrote to Franziska from Port Said, "escapes himself nowhere."

And so he returned home and waited—for what? "We must agree never to see each other again," wrote Franziska, "as long as your wife lives." Haeckel gave his consent to this agreement. And then they met again—and again.

Ardently they both yearned for the day when his wife would leave them free. But they expressed this yearning only by innuendo. "The poor thing," writes Haeckel, "has been in bed again for the past eight weeks. I assure you that I am doubly patient and attentive now." And Franziska, in reply—"You must be very careful of your poor, dear wife. How is her heart? Is there any hope?"

Every day, indeed, the doctors expected his invalid wife's heart to flicker out. . . .

But it was Franziska's heart that gave out. One winter morning Haeckel received a telegram from Ursula Altenhausen. "My sister Franziska died suddenly last night."

VII

HAECKEL LIVED ON for another sixteen years—tragically alone. And then, on a midsummer night in 1919, he fell mercifully asleep. "The riddle of man's life," he wrote a few days before he died, "remains unanswered. But—*impavidi progrediamur,* let us go forward unafraid!"

STEINMETZ

Great Scientific Contributions by Steinmetz

Discovered the law of *hysteresis,* or loss of power, in alternating electric currents.

Formulated method of calculating alternating currents.

INVENTION:
Invented "lightning arrestors" to protect high power transmission lines.

BOOKS, PAMPHLETS AND LECTURES·

On Electric Discharges.

On Engineering and Mathematics.

Relativity and Space.

Radiation, Light and Illumination.

Theory and Calculation.

Steinmetz

Charles Proteus Steinmetz

1865–1923

He was born deformed. The left leg wasn't "just straight" and there was a hump on his back. "But he'll get along all right," the doctor assured his father.

Karl Heinrich stiffened. "Oh yes, he'll get along all right." All the Steinmetzes did. In spite of their handicaps. For generations they had toiled and suffered on the constantly shifting frontiers of Germany and Poland. They had lived by their shrewdness. They had been innkeepers and shopmen, small town bourgeoisie who knew how to bargain and to eke a narrow margin of profit out of life. Never had they asked for quarter. Never fear for the newcomer. "He'll manage somehow."

And within a year little Karl had to manage without his mother. His father, a lithographer for a German railroad, placed him under the care of his grandmother.

In the large room of the house on Tauenzienstrasse in Breslau the frolicsome child played with his *Grossmutter* and learned how far he could exploit her love. She entertained him with folk tales of her native Poland and with biblical stories about the ancient Hebrew cities of splendor and gold.

"We too have miracle cities, have we not, Grossmutter?"

[247]

asked the child. "Perhaps when I grow up I can help to build one of them."

With his wooden blocks he constructed the Temple of Solomon and when grandmother wasn't looking, he set a candle inside "to light it up." But the flame fed on the blocks and threatened to grow into a conflagration until his grandmother rushed over and deluged the building in water.

Karl was hurt and mystified. So *this* is what happens when you try to give too much light. As he grew older, his mind laid plans to seek for a light that would shine in the temple without reducing it to ashes.

He entered the gymnasium at an age when he was "scarcely beyond his infancy." At five he conjugated Latin verbs. At seven he learned Greek and a smattering of Hebrew. At eight he possessed a "respectable knowledge" of algebra and geometry. Upon his completion of ten years of study he was ready to graduate with the highest honors. Nervously he awaited the event.

It was the custom for the graduating class to appear on the platform in full dress and to participate in an oral examination. Karl could not afford to own a formal suit. But he rented one. And then, on the morning before the great occasion there appeared on the bulletin board of the school the following notice:

"Karl August Rudolph Steinmetz, by reason of his exceptional scholarship, is not required to submit to the oral examination."

Slowly he folded his formal suit and put it away. The tears on his cheeks were hot. He understood the reason for his exemption. The crippled body of the student. The crippled minds of the teachers. They were ashamed to show him before the public. They had singled him out, alone among the students, only to make him the more painfully aware of his loneliness.

Karl Steinmetz never wore a full dress suit again.

II

SHORTLY AFTER HE ENTERED the University of Breslau he gave evidence of a prodigious intellect. His professors were amazed at his "magical juggling" of figures. They nicknamed him *Proteus*.

The ancient little hunchback of the sea. According to the Greek legend, Proteus was no bigger than the human hand. When trapped, he could change himself into a thousand different shapes. But if the captor held firm, he would gradually resume his real shape, and whisper into the ear the secrets of the world. For the wrinkled little god possessed all the knowledge that men were searching for. . . . So, too, did this little Proteus of a Steinmetz, said the students with an uneasy smile. They were somewhat afraid of his "uncanny mind."

But Steinmetz craved companionship, and he sought for the society of his more serious fellow students. One day a classmate invited him to tea and told him about the plans of the German workers for a new social order—a world free from want, a coöperative commonwealth whose motto, based upon the Golden Rule, would be, *One for all and all for one*. "Will you join us socialists?" asked his classmate.

Karl's heart leaped with excitement. Here was a young man interested in matters beyond the usual frolics and duels of the average student. Of course he would join him and his socialists!

At first his new "crusade" was a pleasant diversion from his studies. For the early socialism of Germany was a peaceful movement to secure, by political means, many of the reforms that we in America have gained within the past ten years. But due to the arrogant stupidity of Bismarck the movement was driven underground. As a result of this suppression the "cause" of socialism gained momentum. But the members of the socialist party had won the badge of martyrdom.

The "movement" had now become an exciting adventure for Steinmetz. He wrote letters in invisible ink to fellow agitators who were detained by the authorities. He undertook to edit the socialist weekly—*The People's Voice*—with its challenging and somewhat absurd motto: "We don't know what the government wants, but we are against it."

Karl Steinmetz had found congenial company at last. He was a full-fledged member of the "Noble Order of the Dispossessed." Gradually his mathematical problems took up less and less of his time as the "larger social problem" began to occupy the foremost place in his mind.

And just now this problem called for an immediate and personal solution. *The People's Voice* was in financial straits. One day the printer and the paper merchant appeared together demanding the immediate payment of a bill that had been overdue for several months. But Karl's sense of humor didn't desert him. He led his two creditors into the rear office of *The People's Voice* and offered to give them in payment a complete file of the weekly's back numbers. "Very interesting historical matter," he explained, "quite unobtainable elsewhere."

Finally a bailiff appeared to attach the furniture. "May I offer you a complete file of our back numbers?" inquired the intrepid editor. "Quite unobtainable elsewhere."

It was a gay life. And it was coming to an end. For he was about to graduate from college—with the highest honors in mathematics, to the great joy of his father. It was rumored that the authorities were planning to publish his senior thesis in the official scientific journal. A brilliant career was ahead.

One evening Steinmetz rounded up his socialist friends and announced that he wanted to give a beer party in celebration of his success. It was a merry company that swarmed into the restaurant. Each man called for a stein of beer. Each man proposed a toast, to which the entire company responded in chorus. As the evening wore on, the voices grew louder and the humor broader. They sang in complete disorder.

And then Steinmetz proposed a final toast. "To my father, whose greatest desire it has been to see me graduate with honors.

To my escape over the Swiss border from the police who, as I have been tipped off, are planning to arrest me as a socialist. To my senior thesis that might have come to a glorious end in publication rather than in a hideaway suitcase. To the world and its irony, let's drink!"

In the dawn he tiptoed into his father's room. The older man stirred in his sleep. "I have had such a pleasant dream, Karl— your future——"

"Yes, father," he murmured. "My future . . . It *was* a pleasant dream, was it not?"

A few hours later he left Germany and his father forever.

III

AT ZURICH he earned a scant income writing articles on astronomy. He attended courses at the Polytechnic Institute, rooming with a fellow student "on the top floor of the last house at the end of the final street at the edge of the town." And here came an important turn in his life. His fellow lodger, Asmussen, told him of a country which he had visited—"a land of magic" where the "social question" did not exist. "If you came to America you could discard your preoccupation with politics and devote yourself exclusively to mathematics. There is a crying need for engineers in America."

A land of opportunity where everyone was given a second chance—even a cripple who was hounded by the German police. Perhaps in the West he might find the light that glowed but didn't scorch. His roommate had spoken of the Goddess of Liberty who held in her uplifted hand the torch that lighted the gateway of the New World.

It mightn't be a bad idea to sail for America. But how was he to raise the money for the passage?

It was his fellow lodger who—involuntarily—found an answer to the question. He had fallen in love with a Swiss girl and he had written about his "blessed romance" to an uncle who lived in San Francisco and who supplied him with his monthly allowance. The answer was a stern command that Asmussen come to America at once. Furthermore, he gave notice to his nephew that he was cutting off his allowance.

The saddened lover fingered his bank roll reflectively. "I'll pay your expenses to New York, Karl, if you come along with me."

Steinmetz hesitated for an instant. "What can you do here, Karl? You can't return to Germany. The only good business in Switzerland is that of a hotel keeper. Have you got a hotel?"

And so it was decided. They came by steerage. The steamship, *La Champagne,* docked in the New York harbor on a warm June day. The officials looked over the shipload of prospective Americans. They were not at all impressed by the little dwarf of a man who limped up to them. Could he speak English? He didn't understand, didn't answer. Asmussen, who spoke English fluently, interpreted the question. "A few——" mumbled Steinmetz sheepishly.

Had he any money? "Nein." Had he any job? "Nein." Undesirable alien! They would ship him home. No one asked to see the treatise on higher mathematics that he had along with him—a work that singled him out as one of the few geniuses of his generation. To the detention room with him!

But Asmussen stepped in. He showed the officials a bank roll. He asserted that these funds were at the disposal of Steinmetz. "I will personally see to it that my friend does not become a public charge."

The authorities yielded. The unprepossessing young cripple limped up the busy streets of New York, with only a few letters of recommendation to electrical firms, a capital of mathematical symbols and a slender luggage of hope. He moved with Asmussen into a tenement in Brooklyn and started immediately to look for a job. He applied to the chief engineer of the Edison Electric Company and received a curt rebuff. "There are too many engineers coming to America these days."

He visited the manufacturing establishment of Rudolph Eiche-meyer. The secretary, taking him for a tramp, was preparing to shoo him away when Mr Eichemeyer himself strode into the office. The young foreigner made a stumbling attempt to intro-duce himself. Rudolph Eichemeyer looked at him kindly. Here was a fellow German. "Sprechen Sie Deutsch?" Within an hour's conversation he had learned all about Steinmetz. "I too am a political refugee," he remarked. "I fled from Germany in 1848. Come around in a week. There may be a job waiting."

There *was* a job waiting—the position of draughtsman at twelve dollars a week. Eichemeyer was a manufacturer of hats. But in his spare moments he experimented with electrical gadgets of his own devising. "Are you interested in electricity?" he asked Steinmetz. "If so, you may study some of the generators I've been tinkering with. Clumsy contraptions, I admit—elementary attempts to supply the world with power and light. Most of us are still groping blindly in this field. We blunder and stumble and snatch here and there at a little electricity, an incandescent lamp, a wire, but mostly we know nothing about the general laws. We do not as yet understand how to control electricity."

And then he took Steinmetz to a window overlooking the busy street. "There is a throne awaiting some man—a seat of untold power over vast cities and industries and millions of men and women—such is the kingdom of light lying in wait for its law-giver . . ."

Even for a friendless immigrant who had eluded the police in his native land? That night when work was over there was a flush on the face of a little hunchback as he hitched his way home.

IV

WITHIN THREE YEARS Karl Steinmetz had assumed the throne in the kingdom of light. He had joined the American Institute of Electrical Engineers. He had reviewed the notes he had taken on electrical transformers at the Polytechnic in Switzerland. And he had made a thorough study of Eichemeyer's generators. Did the industry need an expert mathematician? The entire realm of mathematics had limped its way to America in that summer month of 1889. The electrical engineers were complaining that they were unable to estimate beforehand the efficiency of any generators which they were planning to build. And this inability to foretell the power capacity of an engine under construction was due to *hysteresis*—an (unpredictable) loss of energy. The engineers had noticed that a current passing through a core of iron sets up a magnetic north pole and a magnetic south pole, and that when the current reverses its direction, so also are the poles reversed. This alternating magnetism, the engineers had further noticed, meant a loss of power and efficiency. But nobody knew how to estimate the amount of this loss in advance and therefore nobody knew how to build a machine that would reduce the *hysteresis* to a minimum. It was a hit-or-miss method, and the misses were far more frequent than the hits.

Such was the electrical state of affairs in the 1880's. A race of engineers in the wilderness of experimental electricity were looking for a Moses to lead them to the promised land of mathematical certainty. But for a long stretch of time no voice spoke to them.

And then at a meeting of the American Institute of Electrical Engineers in January 1892, one of its most obscure members walked to the platform and in halting, broken English read to the assemblage a mathematical paper. In this paper he formulated, definitely and for all time, the exact law of *hysteresis*. No need any longer to build a generator blindly. Karl Steinmetz had tamed electricity to the service of man.

Now he was no longer a German "alien" but an American pioneer. Accordingly he must adopt an American name. *Charles August Rudolph Steinmetz? Charles Rudolph Steinmetz? Charles August Steinmetz?* No—none of these would do—they were too hyphenated. *Charles Steinmetz?* That was better. But still something was wrong. Most Americans, he had noticed, had middle names. And then a puckish laugh shook his little frame of five foot three. Why not *Proteus* for a middle name? The old nickname of his student days. Proteus, the god of a thousand shapes, the guardian of a thousand secrets, the interpreter of the mystery of the tempest and the fire and the sea . . . From that day on, he signed his name *Charles Proteus Steinmetz.*

V

IN THIS SAME YEAR which marked the discovery of the law of *hysteresis* (1892) the Edison General Electric Company of New York merged with a rival company and formed the gigantic trust of the General Electric Works. This new organization bought out the firm of Rudolph Eichemeyer and received, along with its other assets, the services of young Steinmetz. The company moved its general offices to Lynn, Massachusetts, and Steinmetz went to that city together with the rest of the office personnel.

A friend who had known him in New York paid him a visit a month after his removal to Lynn and was amazed to find him in sad straits. His clothes were ragged. He looked pale and thin. He had not paid the rent for his room. Through a clerical oversight his name had been omitted from the payroll. For four weeks he had received no salary and he was too shy to make inquiries. "Perhaps," he told his friend, "they don't think I'm worth a salary as yet. Perhaps they feel that I ought to be grateful for the experience I'm getting with the firm."

It was soon made clear to him, however, that he was not expected to work for nothing. Indeed, he learned that his financial worries were over for the rest of his life. For the executives of the company realized that they had captured a Merlin of the modern age and they would never let him go. They sealed him in comfort and turned the key. The little man blinked in bewilderment as he looked at his new shoes and his new clothes and the platters of tasty meats that were set up before him. He pinched himself to see if he were really awake.

And then, satisfied that this was no dream, he took out his wand and worked another miracle. He had observed that alternating current had gradually begun to replace direct current as the best means of transmitting electricity over great distances. But as a result of this replacement a new difficulty had arisen. It was easy enough to calculate the regular flow of direct current according to Ohm's Law. But no mathematical law had as yet been discovered to measure the irregular flow of alternating current. Steinmetz now discovered this law. It was a mathematical formula that required three volumes of complicated equations.

"This man," declared the chairman of the board of directors, "isn't cut out to be an engineer. He isn't a toolmaker but a lawgiver—a thinker in a class with Newton." From that day on they gave him no orders, made for him no regulations, and classified him for no particular job. "Here is our entire plant. Do anything you want with it. Dream all day, if you wish. We'll pay you for dreaming."

The company moved from Lynn to Schenectady and dressed the city out in a constellation of light. And into this Bagdad on the Mohawk rode the pigmy king in triumph. As the lights streamed from the humming dynamos and a thousand suns danced in the midnight air Steinmetz knew at last that he had come home. This was the miracle shrine that had been awaiting him from his childhood days. Here in the electric city alive with batteries and wires of power devised largely out of his abstract mathematical formulas he sat hunched at the switch—a modern Jehovah ready to wield his thunderbolts over the cities of men. A Jehovah with a little red beard and a stogy in his mouth. A flibbertigibbet of a celebrity. Newsmen cornered him and photographed him and made much ado about "selling" him to the public. But still he was timid. He fancied that people were fascinated by his pisturesque personality rather than by any appreciation of his thoughts or his feelings.

Did they know, for example, why he had moved into a big house on Wendell Avenue? And did they realize how lonely he was in the midst of these luxurious surroundings? At first he had taken lodgings with a landlady. But he was ill at ease. He burnt her carpets with his acids, damaged her walls with his gadgets, ruined her disposition with his noises in his home-made laboratory at all hours of the day and the night. And that was why he had built himself a mansion—a hermitage for the housing of all his laboratory needs, a spacious temple of light. But he trembled at the thought of moving into the vast palace—a king without a family, without a friend. The reporters waxed enthusiastic about the splendor of the house and never bothered themselves about the loneliness of the owner.

But he tried to conquer his loneliness. One evening he paid a visit to his laboratory assistant—a young man who had just taken a wife. Timidly he invited the young couple to come and live with him. "In this way, you see, my house can become a home." Soon there might be a family in this house—children of sounder flesh than his own. Some day, perhaps, they would call him godfather . . .

The young couple accepted his invitation and moved into the house on Wendell Avenue. But Steinmetz still remained alone—shrinking from the company of his fellows who were fashioned so differently from himself. Out of his suffering for his own ugliness he had developed a tenderness toward all ugly things. In the conservatory adjoining his house he cultivated a "distorted paradise"—of cacti plants. No delicate flowers for him. No foliage of beauty. But ugly misshapen cacti. He spent thousands of dollars preserving them in a hothouse against the blasts of winter. People shuddered at his taste.

"If you want to make me really happy," he told his acquaintances, "send me alligators." He built a pool for five of them, and decorated it with lilies. Accompanying him as he limped through the grounds of his estate was a homely mongrel who would never have gained his master's affection had he been slick and pedigreed. "Send me sick fowl and anemic kittens. I will fatten them." The outcast animals reached him in swarms.

And then came the climax to his collection in the "garden of the horrible and the misfit"—a Gila monster. The more curious among the people of Schenectady went to their encyclopedias for an account of this monster. "A huge, sluggish lizard . . . Its head equals the size of its body, and its tail equals the size of its head . . . With its two spearlike teeth it holds on to its victim while the saliva oozes from its venomous mouth . . ."

Such was the gentle pet. Steinmetz kept him in a cage and every year placed a dozen eggs by his side. Once a month the creature roused himself from his slumbers in the sun and ate an egg. And then he shut his scaly eyelids.

Ugly creatures, these. Nobody cared for them, yet somehow they made their way in life. Steinmetz closed his eyes whimsically over his cigar.

VI

HE WAS RAISED (in 1901) to the presidency of the American Institute of Electrical Engineers. The following year he was given an honorary degree at Harvard University. "I confer this degree upon you," said President Eliot, "as the foremost electrical engineer in the United States and therefore in the world."

When George R. Lunn entered upon his term as the socialist mayor of Schenectady, he appointed his fellow socialist of Breslau president of the Board of Education. Steinmetz was happy at the opportunity to put some of his social theories into practice. He increased the number of city playgrounds, he instituted special classes for the mentally slow and for the immigrants unfamiliar with the English language, and he introduced glass-enclosed classrooms on the roofs of the schoolhouses for the tubercular children. "Bring light into the lives of people—a light that does not destroy but only heals."

The skeptics wagged their heads over his social activities. How could this engineer of a great monopoly reconcile his capitalistic profession with his socialistic idealism? In answer to this question Steinmetz wrote a book—*America and the New Epoch*. It is precisely through the expansion of capitalism that we shall bring about state socialism, he declared. From the large scale corporation to the corporate state. "Eventually private ownership will give way to government ownership under private management." And all this, through the peaceful use of the ballot.

He was a great believer in economic reform through political means. In 1922 he ran on the socialist ticket for the office of state engineer. His specific platform was the harnessing of water power. "For this in a large measure means the liberation of man." Puffing vigorously at his cigar he terrified all the lovers of beauty with his proposal that the water of the Niagara Falls be channeled into a huge plant for hydroelectrical purposes. What was the esthetic pleasure of a honeymooning couple as compared to the physical welfare of the human race? He estimated that the potential energy of Niagara Falls was six million horsepower. "This would bring to the state about two billions of dollars annually—to be spent on housing, playgrounds and schools." And then as he enumerated these advantages his face softened into a puckish smile. For a compromise suggestion had occurred to him. On the six working days of the week the water could be diverted to supply the power for the hydroelectric machinery. But on Sundays the power could be closed down and the water could then be allowed to tumble over the precipice "in all its holiday beauty." His eyes beamed with excitement as the full glory—and the full humor—of the vision dawned upon him. "What a spectacle it would make, with the water beginning to trickle, slowly at first, then tumbling more and more impetuously until it became the thundering Niagara that we know! Wouldn't that be a display infinitely more impressive than what we have now?" He was defeated at the polls.

But he went on with his utopian dreams. "The progress of the human race," he once remarked, "is merely a matter of intelligent engineering." And then he went on to cite an example in order to clarify his idea. "If the Bering Strait were blown up and widened and deepened, we would be able to divert the whole course of that current to the north of North America. If that current ran above our continent, it would melt all the ice and snow of Canada and Alaska, and there would be no more glaciers in Greenland or icebergs in the Atlantic. . . . It would make all of North America warmer in the winter and milder in the summer It would double the habitable area of the globe. It would remake the world."

And on another occasion: "I believe that the engineers of the future will bring about a four-hour working day. Work is a curse. The chief aim of society should be the abolition of it."

As for himself, however, he sought no cessation from his work. His beard was graying even as he grew young with his thoughts of the future. The total of cigar stubs that he had thrown away mounted appallingly. And still Steinmetz continued with his experiments.

Now he was studying lightning arrestors—devices to protect electrical machinery from the bolts of an angry sky. Now he was building electric condensers that succeeded in capturing some of the characteristics of these celestial bolts. All around him his associates were clamoring for more power, more light —higher currents to press through the wires—higher voltage!

And now at last Charles Proteus Steinmetz was ready for his final experiment. "Come in, gentlemen," he told the group of reporters and of distinguished scientists who had gathered at the door of his laboratory. "I have manufactured lightning!"

Quietly they entered. In the corner of the room they saw a monster generator. Spread out before them was a miniature village with houses and trees and a white-steepled church. "If you please, gentlemen, I will show you the devastating power of electricity."

There was a subdued hum and a glow in the vacuum tubes as they warmed up to discharge their power. And then—a terrific crash. A zigzag flame broke over the village. The trees and the houses and the steeple were enveloped in a whirlpool of smoke.

As the smoke cleared the trees were dust, the houses were a heap of ruins, and the white steeple of the church had entirely disappeared.

Steinmetz looked at his astonished audience with a whimsical smile. "Incalculable is the power of electricity to destroy," he said, "when wielded by a foolish hand. . . . But equally incalculable, when wielded by a *wise* hand, is the power of electricity to *build*."

VII

SIDE BY SIDE with the cacti the owner of the Wendell House had planted the grounds with orchards lovely and fragrant. But the shadows threatened all the beauty, all the ugliness. Steinmetz was getting old and wayworn. One autumn morning (October 26, 1923) his adopted son, Joseph Hayden, entered the bedroom of the engineer. He had sensed that Dr Steinmetz had passed a restless night. "I'll bring up the breakfast tray," he suggested. "Better to eat a snack before you try to get up."

"All right. I will lie down again."

A few minutes later Hayden's son came into the room with the breakfast. He drew close to the bed. The little man was sound asleep.

Somewhere in the silent air lurked a voice speaking words

that only a little child in Breslau and a kindly old grandmother would understand. "I am tired building with my blocks, Grossmutter. I will lie down again. And when the morning comes, I will make another temple so much better than the one I built today."

MARIE CURIE

Great Scientific Contributions by Marie Curie

Discovered radium, and established its healing power in certain diseases.

BOOKS AND PAPERS:
Radioactivity.
Radiology and War.
The Magnetization of Tempered Steel.

Marie Curie

Marie Curie

1867–1934

IN 1903 MADAME CURIE was the most celebrated woman in the
world. She had just shared the Nobel Prize in Physics together
with Pierre Curie and with Henri Becquerel. Screaming head-
lines in the newspapers, thousands of letters from autograph
seekers, innumerable requests for lectures, messages from "departed spirits" forwarded through the "collaboration" of trance
mediums, banquets, honors, titles, reporters, photographers,
curiosity hunters—all these had descended upon her in an
avalanche of unwelcome hosannas. Manufacturers of popular
articles solicited her endorsement. A horse breeder asked for her
permission to name his favorite horse after her. For many years
the spotlight of public adulation kept singling her out as the
foremost of public characters—save one. As she got out of a
train to deliver a lecture in Berlin one day, she was pleasantly
surprised to find herself alone. The mob had stormed to another
part of the platform where Jack Dempsey was getting out of the
same train. The world's champion physicist was not quite so important a personage as the world's champion pugilist.

Madame Curie thoroughly despised the distinctions and the
distractions of glory. She regarded herself as a captive chained

and led unwillingly in a triumphal procession. She threw away her caps and her gowns and her titles and her medals as soon as she got them. The only things she kept were the menus from the banquets at which she sat as a martyred guest. "These menus, made of thick, hard cardboard, are so convenient for scribbling down my mathematical calculations."

Speaking of this most modest of celebrated women, the most modest of celebrated men—Albert Einstein—once remarked: "Marie Curie is, among all distinguished people, the only one whom fame has not corrupted."

II

MANYA SKLODOVSKA, known today as Marie Curie, came of a Polish stock of noble and honest peasants. Her parents had risen above the soil into the rarefied atmosphere of higher education. Her father was a professor of physics at the Warsaw High School, and her mother was an accomplished pianist. Manya— a pet name for Marya—inherited her father's brains and her mother's hands. She showed an early aptitude for experimental science. But her parents didn't allow any of their five children to do much studying. There was a taint of consumption in the family. Whenever Manya became absorbed in her books, Madame Sklodovska would put her hand gently on the child's head. "Go and play in the garden, Manyusha. It's so beautiful outside."

Every evening at their prayers the children added a final sentence: "And please, God, restore our mother's health."

But it pleased God to take Madame Sklodovska from her children—there were four now; one of them had died of typhus. Manya was only ten when she was left motherless.

It was a sad and impoverished family that gathered around the table after Madame Sklodovska's departure. Manya's father had lost his position in the high school because of his aspiration

MARIE CURIE

for the freedom of Poland from the tyranny of the Russian czar.
He had opened a boarding school, but with indifferent success.
The maintenance of his family seemed a task beyond his feeble
powers. Four healthy mouths to be fed, four growing bodies to
be clothed, and four active minds to be educated. Desperately he
invested his inadequate savings in the hope that the numerator
of his possessions might grow equal to the denominator of his
needs. But he lost his entire investment. He had nothing to look
forward to.

Nothing but four children with superior brains and superior
grit. All these children were destined to rise from poverty to
achievement. For the strength of the Polish soil was within them.

And the aspiration of the Polish heart. The aspiration of a
free soul in a chained body. The Sklodovski children, like their
father, were rebels. They fought against adversity and they
fought against tyranny. Every morning when Manya walked to
school, she passed by a statue dedicated "to the Poles faithful to
their Sovereign"—that is, to the Poles who were faithless to their
country. Manya always made it a point to spit upon this statue.
If, by inadvertence, she failed to perform this act of disrespect,
she turned back to make good her failure—even at the risk of
coming late to school.

This gallant little rebel expressed her contempt for oppression
not only in the absence but also in the presence of her oppres-
sors. Among her teachers who represented the alien governing
power over Poland was Mademoiselle Mayer, the German super-
intendent of studies. This "slithering spy with her muffled slippers" was a little bit of a woman with a prodigious capacity for
hate. She made life unbearable for her Polish pupils—especially
for "that Sklodovska girl" who dared to answer her lashing
tongue with a scornful smile. But Manya was not always content
with a mere smile of silent scorn. One day "the spy" attempted,
with a none too gentle hand, to straighten Manya's unruly
Polish curls into a conventional Gretchen braid. In vain. Man-

ya's hair, like her spirit, refused to yield to the tyrant's touch. Exasperated at "the capricious head and the contemptuous eyes" of her Polish pupil, Mayer finally shouted:

"Stop staring at me like that! I forbid you to look down upon me!"

Whereupon Manya, who was a head taller than Mayer, replied sweetly: "I can't very well do anything else, Mademoiselle."

Yet in spite of her rebellion Manya carried off the gold medal at the completion of her high school course (in 1883). It had become a habit with the Sklodovskis to win this highest award for scholarship. There were by this time three gold medals in the family.

And now, said her father, enough of study for the present. Let her go to the country for a year and build up her body. "This pretty child must not, like her mother, fall a victim to consumption."

Manya gladly consented to her father's suggestion. For she loved her play as she loved her work. She yielded herself "body and soul" to the luxury of idleness. "My dear little devil," she wrote to her school friend, Kazia, "I can hardly believe there is any such thing in existence as geometry or algebra." She spent her summer days roaming in the woods, swinging, swimming, fishing, playing battledore and shuttlecock, or just lying on the grass and reading—"no serious books, I assure you, but only absurd and harmless little novels." And she spent her winter nights and days—dancing. Those Polish dances! Starting at sunset and continuing in relays as the revelers, with the fiddlers at their head, journeyed from farmhouse to farmhouse, dancing away the night, beyond the dawn, beyond the sunset of the following day and into the sunrise of the next. And the most tireless as well as the most graceful dancer of them all was Manya Sklodovska. "All the young men from Cracow asked me to dance with them . . . very handsome boys . . . you can't imagine how delightful it was . . . It was eight o'clock of the (second) morning when we danced the last dance—a white mazurka." And then she had to throw away her slippers of russet leather, for "their soles had ceased to exist . . ."

III

AFTER HER YEAR'S VACATION she returned to Warsaw and to an uncertain future. Her older sister, Bronya, wanted to study at the Sorbonne, in Paris. So too did Manya. But there weren't enough funds in the family to finance even one of them, let alone both, through the university. An insoluble problem, it seemed, yet Manya found the solution. "I will get a job as governess and help you through college. Then you will get a doctor's degree and help me in return."

It seemed an audacious plan, but it worked. Manya became a "teaching servant" in the family of Madame B——, a stupid, vulgar and intolerant woman who economized on oil for the lamps and who gambled away her money on cards. "My existence," wrote the young governess, "has become unbearable . . . I shouldn't like my worst enemy to live in such a hell." Fortunately she was able to exchange this for a better position in a somewhat more intelligent home. Her new "mistress," Madame Z——, was fully as intolerant though not quite so vulgar as her former employer. "Madame Z—— has a bad temper, but she is not at all a bad woman . . . Some of her children—she has a whole collection of them—are really delightful."

Especially Casimir, the eldest son. A university student at Warsaw, he had come home for vacation and had promptly fallen in love with the pretty little Sklodovska who not only could talk like a scholar but who could dance like a goddess. And Manya, affectionate and sensitive and lonely, returned his love.

But there was to be no marriage between them. Casimir's mother refused to accept a governess into her family—forgetting that she herself had been a governess before her marriage. For a time Manya played with the idea of suicide. "I have buried all my plans, sealed and forgotten them," she wrote to one of her cousins. "The walls are too strong for the heads that try to break them down . . . I mean to say farewell to this contemptible world. The loss will be small, and regret for me will be short . . ."

She got over her despondency, however. The Sklodovskis were not the suicide type. She returned to her teaching and her scrimping and continued to support Bronya at the Sorbonne. The latter, thanks to Manya's assistance and to an inborn talent for enduring the pangs of hunger, succeeded in starving and studying her way through to a medical degree. She married Casimir Dluski, a fellow student in medicine, and was now ready to conclude her half of the bargain with Manya. The young governess was able at last to see the fulfilment of her most ardent dream. The Sorbonne!

IV

MARIE SKLODOVSKA—she had registered her first name in the French manner—student in the Faculty of Science—age, 23—hair, ashen-blonde—personality, taciturn—ability, exceptional. She always sat in the front row at the lectures; but the moment the lectures were over, she glided out like a shadow. Her sad experience with the social conventions had planted within her an aversion for all sorts of society. "Fine hair, fine eyes, fine figure of a girl," remarked the boys at the university. "But the trouble is, she won't talk to anybody."

For four years "she led the life of a monk." Refusing to be a burden to her sister, she lived alone. She had hired, at fifteen francs (about $3) a month, a sixth-floor attic in the Latin Quarter. The only light came in through a loophole in the slanted ceiling. The room had no heat and no water. In this prison of a room she lived upon a general diet of bread and butter and tea—with the luxury of an egg or a fruit thrown in on the rarest of occasions. In the winter she put a handful of coal into a toy stove and sat doing her equations with numb fingers long after the fire had gone out. Then, at about two in the morning, she crept into an iron bed with insufficient covers.

One day a classmate reported to the Dluskis that Manya had fainted in front of her. Casimir hurried to her attic where he found her at work on her next day's lessons.

"What did you eat today?"

Manya looked up with an evasive smile. "Today? I don't remember."

"Come, come, Manya. No evasions. What did you eat today?"

"Oh, cherries . . . and everything."

Finally he got the confession out of her. For the past twenty-four hours she had lived on a handful of radishes and half a pound of cherries. Much against her will he carried her off to his house where Bronya fed her and rested her up for a few days. And then, in spite of all the protestations of the Dluskis, she returned to her attic and her hunger and her books.

She lived in the world of her books. And of her lectures. In spite of her poverty and her hunger, she felt like an intrepid explorer adventuring over an unfamiliar sea. And she meant to make every mile of it familiar as she kept journeying from day to day to an ever expanding horizon. Physics, chemistry, mathematics, poetry, music, astronomy—the entire circle of the earth and the heavens had come within the range of her intellectual domain. But above all she was interested in her experiments. She regarded the laboratory as a delicate musical instrument upon the keys of which, with the skillful fingers inherited from her mother, she kept constantly seeking to combine old notes into new tunes.

Her professors, delighted with her imagination and her enthusiasm and her skill, kept encouraging her to undertake new researches. And one day, emboldened by her success, she declared that she would carry her special researches not into one but into two fields. She would try for a double master's degree—in physics and in mathematics.

And she succeeded. She passed first in the master's examination in physics (1893), and second in the master's examination in mathematics (1894).

A brief vacation in Poland, and then back to Paris—and to her second love affair. After her first unfortunate plunge into the whirlpool of romantic passion, she had vowed to dedicate the rest of her life to a single passion for science. She had no use for men.

And at that time there lived in Paris a young man, Pierre Curie, who had no use for women. He, too, had devoted his life to the exclusive pursuit of science.

One day they met at the apartment of M. Kovalski, a Polish professor of physics who was visiting Paris. "When I came in," wrote Marie, "Pierre Curie was standing in the window recess near a door leading to the balcony. He seemed very young to me, although he was then aged thirty-five. I was struck by the frank expression of his eyes and by a slight appearance of carelessness in his tall figure. I liked his slow, reflective words, his simplicity and his smile, at once grave and youthful. We started to converse on matters of science . . . and before we knew it we were friends."

Pierre Curie, the son of a French physician, had become a bachelor of science at sixteen and a master of physics at eighteen. When he met Marie, he was head of the laboratory at the Parisian School of Chemistry and Physics. His achievements had already placed him in the front rank of French scientists. He had formulated the principle of symmetry in the structure of crystals. Together with his brother Jacques he had discovered the important phenomenon of piezoelectricity—that is, the generation of electricity by means of pressure. He had invented a new apparatus for the precise measurement of minute quantities of electricity. And he had constructed an ultra-sensitive instrument —known as the *Curie Scale*—for checking the results of scientific experiments.

For all these achievements he was receiving from the French

State the miserable salary of three hundred francs (about $60) a month.

On this inadequate salary he timidly proposed marriage to Mademoiselle Sklodovska; and Mademoiselle Sklodovska—with equal timidity, it must be confessed—accepted.

Yet the marriage turned out to be not only a partnership of genius but also a comradeship of love. After an unconventional wedding without a lawyer or a priest—both of them were free-thinkers—they enjoyed an equally unconventional honeymoon bicycling over the country roads of the Ile-de-France. Then they returned to Paris and settled down to the work which was to bring glory to the name of Curie and healing to an afflicted world.

V

MARIE TOOK CARE of the house, gave birth to a baby girl, then to another, studied for her doctorate in physics, won a fellowship with a monograph on the magnetization of tempered steel, and spent all the rest of her time collaborating with her husband in his experiments. The doctors warned her of a tubercular lesion in the left lung—the Sklodovski family taint. They advised her to go to a sanatorium. But Marie wouldn't think of it. She was too deeply absorbed in her laboratory work. She and Pierre had become interested in the experiments of Henri Becquerel. This eminent French physicist, while examining the salts of a "rare metal," uranium, had discovered that these salts emitted a ray which apparently could penetrate opaque objects. A compound of uranium, which he had placed on a photographic plate sur-rounded by black paper, had made an impression on the plate *through* the paper. This, so far as we know, was the first human observation of the penetrating quality of certain strange types of rays.

What was the nature of this mysterious property of penetra-tion through opaque objects? And whence came this peculiar energy? These questions exercised a tremendous fascination upon the minds of Marie and Pierre Curie. Here was a subject for original study, a thesis worthy indeed of a doctor's degree at the Sorbonne!

Such was the enthusiastic yet humble beginning of the research that led to the discovery of radium. Marie had started out on the road to an ordinary doctorate. She found at the end of the road —the Nobel Prize in Physics.

But the traveling of the road was long and arduous and heart-breaking. It took a man and a woman of supreme imagination and of supreme courage to go on unfalteringly to the end.

Almost from the first they encountered insurmountable difficulties—and they surmounted them. The laboratory that the director of the School of Physics gave them for their experiments was an old and dilapidated woodshed. In this damp and cold shanty of a workroom—in the winter the temperature of the laboratory averaged about 44°—the consumptive little pioneer and her husband plunged resolutely into the unknown. With their pitiably inadequate apparatus they examined the nature of uranium and discovered that the mysterious radiation of this metal was an *atomic* property. And then the light of a great thought fell upon Marie. Perhaps uranium was not the only chemical element that possessed the power of irradiation. Perhaps there were other substances with even greater powers of "penetrating the impenetrable." She must try and see . . .

And so another and even more daring venture into uncharted seas. Madame Curie took up all the known chemical bodies and submitted them, one by one, to a rigorous test. And before long she discovered what she was after. Uranium was *not* the only element with that mysterious power of irradiation. Another element, thorium, possessed the same power in about the same degree. To this power Madame Curie now gave the name of *radioactivity*—the active and *penetrating* property of certain types of rays.

But this was only the beginning of her research. In her examination of some of the compounds of uranium and of thorium she had found a *far more powerful* radioactivity than could have been expected from the quantity of uranium or of thorium contained in the compounds. Whence came this extra power of radiation? To this question there was but a single answer—the compounds must have contained a chemical element whose radioactivity was far greater than that of uranium or of thorium. But Madame Curie had already examined all the *known* chemical elements and had found no such powerful radioactivity in any of them. Therefore, she concluded, there must be a hitherto unknown element that possessed this power. *A new element.*

With beating heart she went to see her sister one day. "You know, Bronya, the radiation that I couldn't explain comes from a new chemical element. The element is there and I've got to find it!"

And now she set about the business of finding this new substance. It was in the pitchblende ore—an oxid of uranium—that she had noticed the tremendous power of radiation. Somewhere in this ore lurked the mysterious source of this power. The radioactive part of pitchblende, thought Madame Curie, must represent an exceedingly small fraction of the ore in its crude state, since no scientist before her had ever been able to discover it. Perhaps this new element would be found to consist of not more than one per cent of the pitchblende, concluded the cautious young Polish scientist. How great would have been her astonishment had she then realized that the new element she was trying to isolate consisted of only *one ten-thousandth of one per cent,* or *a millionth part,* of the pitchblende ore!

Marie and Pierre—they had always worked together on these researches—were now certain that they were on the threshold of a new discovery. But how to get beyond the threshold? Pitchblende, out of which they hoped to isolate their new element, was an expensive ore. It was mined in Bohemia for the extraction of the uranium salts that were used in the manufacture of glass. A ton of pitchblende, with the uranium that it contained, was far beyond the Curie pocketbook. It was a problem that seemed beyond solution.

But they solved it. If the new element, they reasoned, existed in the pitchblende and was yet different from uranium, then it could be isolated from the *residue* of the pitchblende *after* the uranium had been extracted. This residue was regarded as almost worthless. The Curies could have considerable quantities of it for little more than the cost of transportation.

And so these "queer" scientists, to everybody's amusement, began to order tons upon tons of "rubbish" to be shipped to their woodshed. And when this "rubbish" arrived they began to throw it, shovel by shovel, into an old cast-iron stove with a rusty pipe. For four years they kept at it like a couple of stokers in the hold of a ship—shoveling, gasping, coughing at the noxious fumes, forgetful of their discomfort and intent upon a single thought— to lure the secret of the new element out of the blazing metal.

And finally they lured out the secret—two secrets. For instead of one they found two new elements—a substance which they named *polonium* after Marie's native country, and another substance which they called *radium*.

The nature of polonium was amazing enough. Its radioactivity was ever so much more powerful than that of uranium. But the nature of radium was the eighth great wonder of the world. For its power of radiation was found to exceed that of uranium by *one and a half million per cent*.

VI

IT WAS CUSTOMARY for the recipients of the Nobel Prize to call for it in person at Stockholm. But the Curies were unable to make the journey. They were too ill. Quietly, modestly, humbly they went on with their work—and with their privations. They spent all their money on their further experiments and remained gloriously forgetful of their personal interests. When the therapeutic value of radium was established—it had been found effective, among other things, in the treatment of cancer—their friends urged upon them the necessity of patenting the process of extracting radium. To do so would have meant considerable wealth to the Curies, since radium was valued at $150,000 a gram. But they refused to derive any income from their discovery. "Radium is an instrument of mercy and it belongs to the world."

They refused not only profits but honors as well. All they asked of the world was to give them a good workroom for their experiments. When the dean of the Sorbonne wrote to Pierre that the Minister had proposed his name for the Legion of Honor, Pierre—seconded by Marie—replied as follows: "Please be so kind as to thank the Minister and to inform him that I do not feel the slightest need of being decorated, but that I am in the greatest need of a laboratory."

On one occasion, however, Pierre did allow his name to be presented for distinction. His scientific colleagues had insisted that he become a candidate for the Academy of Science—not so much for the sake of the honor itself as for the opportunity it would bring him to secure a professorship at the Sorbonne. *And a laboratory.*

Reluctantly he started out upon his round of visits to the members of the Academy. It was the regular custom for every candidate to make these calls and to "drum up" his own qualifications for the honor. Here is how one of the Parisian journalists describes Pierre Curie's "campaign" for the Academy: "To climb stairs, ring, have himself announced, explain why he had come —all this sordidness filled him with shame in spite of himself. But what was even worse, he had to set forth his distinctions, declare the good opinion he had of himself and boast of his knowledge and of his achievements—ordeals which seemed to him beyond human endurance. Consequently he extolled his opponent sincerely and at length, saying that M. Amagat was much better qualified than he, Curie, to enter the Academy . . ."

The Academy elected M. Amagat.

Pierre Curie was highly successful in his efforts to escape from fame. So, too, was Marie. Her simple disguise for avoiding recognition was to remain undisguised. Nobody at first sight would have suspected that the young peasant woman in her unassuming black dress was the celebrated winner of the Nobel Prize. One day an American reporter, hot on the trail of the Curies, had heard that they were spending their vacation in Le Pouldu, a fishing village of Brittany. Arriving at the village, he inquired his way to the Curie cottage. He found a rather unassuming young woman sitting barefoot on the doorstep.

"Are you the housekeeper in this place?"

"Yes."

"Is the lady inside?"

"No, she is out."

"Do you expect her in soon?"

"I don't think so."

"Could you tell me something intimate about her?" asked the reporter as he sat down on the doorstep.

"Nothing," replied Marie, "except one message that Madame Curie told me to convey to reporters: *Be less inquisitive about people, and more inquisitive about ideas.*"

VII

FINALLY Pierre Curie was accepted into the society of his inferior —and therefore envious—fellow scientists. "I find myself in the Academy without having desired to be there and without the Academy's desire to have me."

After several meetings with his colleagues he wrote to a friend: "I have not yet discovered what is the purpose of the Academy."

Yet it served one good purpose—it enabled Pierre to get an appointment to the Sorbonne. Together with the appointment came the offer of a well equipped laboratory. The lifelong dream of the Curies was about to be fulfilled.

And then, one rainy morning in April, 1906, Pierre left his home to visit his publisher. A few hours later they brought his lifeless body to Marie. He had slipped on the wet pavement, and a heavy truck had run over him.

Marie's happiness was at an end. But not her work. She accepted an offer to assume her husband's professorship at the Sorbonne—it was the first time in French history that a position in higher education had been granted to a woman. She went on with her experiments in Pierre's new laboratory, of which she had now become the director. She took care of her children. She prepared papers on her researches. And every night, before going to bed, she wrote an intimate account of her thoughts to her dear departed. It was as if she were writing a letter to someone still alive.

"I am offered the post of successor to you, my Pierre; your course and the direction of your laboratory. I have accepted. I don't know whether this is good or bad . . ."

"My Pierre, I think of you without end. My head is bursting with it and my reason is troubled. I can not understand that I am to live henceforth without you . . ."

"My little Pierre, I want to tell you that the laburnum is in flower, the wistaria, the hawthorn and the iris are beginning— you would have loved all that . . ."

"I no longer love the sun or the flowers. The sight of them makes me suffer. I feel better on dark days like the day of your death, and if I have not learned to hate fine weather it is because my children have need of it . . ."

It was for her children's sake that she went on—and for humanity's sake. A little more work to lessen the sufferings of her fellows. In 1911, when she received the Nobel Prize for the second time, she accepted it merely as another opportunity to widen the scope of her researches. The healing power of radium —this now was the paramount quest of her life. When the World War of 1914 broke out, she organized and personally supervised a number of X-ray outfits for the treatment of wounded soldiers.

Throughout the length and breadth of the country she journeyed —an angel of mercy with a beautiful white face and with pained and acid-bitten fingers.

In spite of her fatigue and her pain and her sorrow she was always ready with her encouraging smile and her gentle word. "Will it hurt?" asked the frightened soldiers when they saw the formidable X-ray apparatus. "Not at all," was her invariable reply. "It's just like taking a photograph."

The war was over. Travels, distinctions, interviews, medals, lectures, banquets—and labor and sorrow. And, to the very end, an "incurable inaptitude" for material success. "Dreamers," she said, "do not deserve wealth, because they do not desire it."

She was now approaching the end of her dream. "Ah, how tired I am!" she murmured as she came home from her laboratory one day. The next morning she couldn't rise from her bed. The doctors who came to examine her were unable to diagnose her disease. It resembled influenza, tuberculosis, pernicious anemia—yet it was none of these. Not until after her death did they discover the real nature of her illness. It was "radium poisoning"—the gradual decay of the vital organs through a lifetime of excessive radiation.

Madame Curie had died a martyr to her work.

BANTING

Great Scientific Contribution by Banting

Discovered the value of insulin in the treatment of diabetes.

Wrote various papers on this discovery.

Banting

Frederick Grant Banting

1891–1941

THE shells burst under the impulse of a heavy bombardment. The Canadian regulars were giving the Boche as much as they took. Men stared grotesquely from the mud at Cambrai —wanting eyes, wanting limbs, wanting souls. Bodies lay promiscuously with alien bodies in the last embrace of death, crushed and twisted beyond recognition. . . .

The blood trickled in a little stream from the lips of young Fred Banting. He was breathing hard, dreaming fitfully. In his delirium he imagined himself bending over the hoe on his father's farm in Alliston, Ontario. The sun was hot, frying his feet in the soil; the perspiration streamed over his face. There, now! He paused to wipe his lips with the back of his arm. Gradually his eyes cleared. This was no farm. This was a hospital. He was stiff on his back. Around him lay boys and men in pain.

"Hello, son. We've got to operate." It was the army doctor's voice.

Banting turned over on his side. "You're not going to take my arm away from me. Not if I can help it, sir!"

They might as well tell him the truth. He was serving with

the army medical corps of the 44th battalion. These boys knew how to take it.

"We must amputate, my boy. Otherwise we may not be able to save your life."

"Oh no, not my arm. I'll risk the chance of dying."

A stubborn, fighting fool. Those were the words that described him best. Back in 1915 he had left his medical course at the University of Toronto and had rushed off to enlist as a private. But they had ordered him back to his education. He would be more serviceable to his country with his medical degree. In 1916 he had joined up again as a doctor. You couldn't argue with these farm lads. They were not used to being answered back when they did their thinking in the fields. They stood on their rights as tenaciously as they rode their plows.

"You see, Doctor, I'm a surgeon myself and I need all the limbs God gave me for the service."

The doctor shrugged his shoulders and moved on to other beds, to other hospitals filled with ruined daring men.

Fred Banting "risked his chance"—and lived.

II

HE RETURNED HOME from the war as quietly as he had left. He entered the Toronto Children's Hospital as resident surgeon. It was fun patching up sick bodies, giving human beings another chance at life. In Flanders he had seen the work of a mighty hand of destruction—inflicting wounds, but never healing them. "It is like the ingenious technique of a Great Surgeon gone mad."

But, after all, Fred Banting was a physician and not a philosopher. He couldn't afford the time to bother about the problems of the Higher Operating Room. He was far too busy with his own problems. And so he merely shrugged his shoulders and put together the bits of broken bones and tied the muscles and straightened out the legs and the arms as best he could.

And then he decided to set up for himself. He moved to London, Ontario, hung out his shingle, and waited. Within the first thirty days only one patient rang the bell. Banting's income for the month amounted to exactly four dollars. "Seems I'm not going to be successful," he smiled grimly. "But at any rate I'm fool enough to be stubborn."

Whatever happened, he would remain stubborn until the day he died.

III

THE WESTERN ONTARIO MEDICAL SCHOOL accepted his services as "part time" lecturer in pharmacology. It was a field of which he had but a limited knowledge. In a literal sense he regarded himself as a student rather than as a teacher. One day he was called upon to prepare a lecture on diabetes. All over the world there were millions of diabetics who "tried in vain to live by starving." For diabetes was listed as "one of the fatal diseases—remedy unknown." Banting secured the literature on the subject. He read a number of articles, prepared his notes and turned in for the night. But he was unable to rest. Wave after wave of drowsiness swept over him, only to recede before the ever recurring question: "Why is it that some bodies, unlike all others, are unable to burn the sugar content in their blood and to transform it into fuel?" It was due, of course, to a defect in their pancreas—that elongated gland which secreted the fermentive juices and which digested the food into bodily energy. But what caused this defect? Take the case of Joe Gilchrist, for example. He was one of the millions starving to death as a result of this mysterious disease. Joe Gilchrist was his friend, and a doctor like himself. They had played marbles and wrestled and attended medical school together. And now he was slowly dying, helpless, feeling the acetone odor on his breath. . . .

"Oh well, there's no help for it, I suppose." And yet . . .

"Scattered on the healthy pancreas are dark spots like little islands." They must be there for a precise reason. Yes, but precisely for *what* reason? Just what was the nature of these pancreatic spots? Again and again the doctors had tried to isolate and to analyze them—but in vain. They had noticed only one definite fact—that the "island spots" of a patient who had died from diabetes were found to have shriveled up to a fraction of their normal size, while those of a patient who had died from other causes were found to have retained their original size. Such was the fact. As to the reason for this fact, nobody could explain it.

Banting tossed and turned that night, as the problem tantalized him. He was stubborn, terribly stubborn. Those mysterious islands, he felt, contained the solution to the problem of diabetes. And he meant to find this solution.

Suddenly an idea set his brain humming. For a few moments he attempted to "spark the gap" between the idea and the delicious wave of drowsiness that was descending upon him. And then he drifted off to sleep.

The following morning he arrived at the office of his superior. "Professor Macleod," he said, "I would like ten dogs and an assistant."

The shrewd old professor looked up from his desk. "Are you bent on a surgical experiment? I think we can grant your request."

"It has nothing to do with surgery, sir. I've a hunch I can reduce the fatality of diabetes."

Professor Macleod laughed good-naturedly. "Every year at the spring fever season some young doctor comes to me with a cure for diabetes."

"I believe I can find a way to check it," persisted Banting. "At least I want to try. I would like to conduct experiments on the pancreas."

"The world's greatest physiologists have been experimenting for years on the pancreas. And what is the sum total of their achievements? They've concocted a starvation diet to torture the victim slowly to death."

"I'm stubborn, Doctor Macleod."

"Have you had the necessary training to conduct experiments in physiology? To speak bluntly, what do you know about diabetic research?"

"Practically nothing, sir. That is why I shall need a specialist to assist me."

"Very well, Banting, you may go ahead."

IV

WHEN BANTING'S FRIENDS and associates heard of his plans they begged him not to abandon his surgical opportunities for a fantastic experiment. At first he listened to them. He returned to his classroom in London, Ontario—for one winter. At the approach of spring he stood in a stuffy little alcove at the Medical Building in Toronto—"a self-appointed researcher, untitled, unpaid." He had taken down his shingle, disposed of his surgical instruments, sold his furniture. For he knew that his research was not to be the matter of a few weeks. His equipment was worse than inadequate—it was simply nonexistent. His only laboratory was a bench. And his training was no better than his equipment. Never in his life had he undertaken an original experiment.

Nevertheless it was with high hopes that he faced his assistant—Charles Herbert Best—a medical student barely out of his teens. This youngster had shown aptitude in chemistry. He would know how to analyze the sugar content in the blood and the urine. And Banting himself would do all the necessary surgical work on the dogs.

Enthusiastically the two young men set to work. Fred Banting had read in a medical journal that if you tie off a pancreas duct, the digestive juice cells "shrivel up and die." This gave him an idea. He would get the digestive juices of the pancreas out of the way and he would thus isolate and study the mysterious "insular spots" which apparently contained the key to the solution of diabetes. "I have a theory, Charlie, that the island cells supply the fuel which burns up the excess of sugar in the healthy body. When this fuel fails, the sugar multiplies and the body becomes diabetic." His logic seemed to him infallible. "Our job, therefore, is to tie off the pancreatic ducts of our dogs, to wait several weeks for the degeneration of the juices, and then to remove and to analyze the residue—or the *soup*—of the island spots."

They started experimenting on their dogs. From ten the number had risen to ninety-one. But still no results. And then, when they were experimenting on their ninety-second dog, a miracle happened. The dog, whose pancreas they had removed, lay dying of diabetes. A shot of the "island" extract, and the sugar in his blood began to decrease. A few hours later the dog was on his feet, barking and wagging his tail.

Banting was jubilant. He had discovered the elixir of life for diabetics. He had been right in his theory. It *was* the extract from the pancreatic "islands" that burned up the poison of excessive sugar in the body. He called this extract *isletin*—which means *island chemical*.

Their experiments were at an end, thought the two young scientists. But they were mistaken. Their miracle proved to be short-lived. Within twenty days the dog was dead of excessive sugar.

What had happened? They hadn't given the dog enough *isletin*. They hadn't been able to *secure* enough. This "island extract" was as unattainable in large quantities as the rarest of minerals. "We've been experimenting with an elixir of our dreams."

But Banting was still hopeful of ultimate success. One day as he sat in his laboratory his thoughts went back to his father's farm in Ontario. A hard, patient, stubborn life—this constant succession of sowing and weeding and harvesting and looking after the cattle . . .

That was it—the cattle! He knew now where he would get his isletin in sufficient quantities to prolong the life of diabetics. He would extract the necessary juices from the unborn calves. The pancreas of an animal in its embryonic stage consisted almost entirely of "island spots." The other digestive juice cells had not as yet developed beyond the rudimentary stage. Here was a great gift to humanity—in the bodies of unborn cattle.

And of *slaughtered* cattle. The pancreatic glands of the animals killed in the shambles had been thrown away as so much rubbish. Now this "rubbish" would become an important factor in the saving of life, thought Banting.

And he was right. With the help of the isletin extracted from the unborn and the slaughtered cattle he succeeded in keeping diabetic dogs alive for an indefinite period. Banting had discovered a positive check if not a complete cure for diabetes in animals. There remained but a single—and fateful—question: Would isletin check diabetes in human beings?

One day, as he was walking in the street, Banting came across his old classmate, Joe Gilchrist. The poor fellow was rapidly "wasting away in streams of sugar." He was emaciated and pallid and hopeless, for he had reached the last stages of the disease.

Banting looked at his friend. "Hello, Joe."

The answer came in a flat, dispirited voice. "Hello, Fred."

"I'd like you to come over to my laboratory, Joe. I've been busy with some experiments that will interest you." Fred Banting's feelings, however, did not reflect the confidence of his voice as he led Joe Gilchrist to the laboratory. He gave his friend an injection of glucose, and then followed it with a shot of isletin. "Let us see now whether the extract will burn up the glucose."

Two hours passed slowly. Gilchrist breathed into the Douglas "test bag." Banting's assistant tested the sick man's breath and looked quietly at Banting. And Banting knew Best's message. There was no sign of change in Joe. He wasn't burning the sugar they had fed him. His breath was heavy and it came in gasps. Banting could not bear to look into his friend's eyes. He rose, gave Best some instructions and left the laboratory. He boarded a train and sped north to Ontario. Here he would spend a few days with his folks and bury his mind in the stillness of the farm. But the click of the wheels over the rails pounded into his consciousness with terrible force. The ticking away of the moments of a man dying from too much sugar . . .

The telephone rang in the Banting farmhouse. It was Joe Gilchrist at the other end. He was talking rapidly, excitedly, to Banting. There was a cheerful lift to his voice. "Right after you left yesterday I started to breathe easily. My head cleared. My appetite returned. Today, to be sure, my legs are dragging again. I'm tired, but I'm not worried. I'm coming back for another shot of that extract . . . The elixir of life . . ."

V

WHEN PROFESSOR MACLEOD heard of Banting's success he immediately gave up all his other duties and took personal charge of the experiments. He changed the name *isletin* to its Latinized equivalent, *insulin*. Like wildfire the news spread that a check for diabetes had at last been found.

Professor Macleod came before the Association of American Physicians and read an official report of the experiments that had been conducted in "my medical laboratories." At the conclusion of the report a voice from the audience called out: "We move that the Association tender to Dr Macleod and his assistants a rising vote expressing its appreciation of his achievement."

Fred Banting was not a bit concerned over this misplaced honor. But he was very much concerned over the condition of his patients. Crowds of them were being brought into Toronto begging for insulin to save their life. But there was not yet enough to go around. Nor was the method of its injection as yet perfected. Joe Gilchrist was still dying. Banting pleaded for money and more money to carry on with his experiments.

He now did most of his work in the diabetic ward of the Christie Street Hospital for Returned Soldiers. Here he walked from bed to bed and injected the precious extract into the veins of those who were most hopelessly sick. The patients suffered no illusions. They knew they were taking terrible risks, for insulin was a two-edged sword. In large doses it lowered the sugar content of the blood to such a degree that the patient suffered a violent shock, fell into convulsions and died. In order to avoid this shock it was necessary to balance the lowering of the sugar with an injection of glucose. But as yet the adjustment of this delicate balance was a matter of trial and error.

The soldiers, however, were not afraid. Expecting death in any case, they were willing to offer themselves as the objects of his experiments. "There's always the chance that this time it may work."

Joe Gilchrist was chief of the "rabbits" for Banting's experiments. He, too, was now a patient at the hospital. The other patients called him *Captain*. Whatever is good enough for Captain is good enough for us.

And little by little Banting was getting results. His "boys" were eating better, were gaining weight. Reports from other clinics began to pour into headquarters. Fifty diabetics in advanced stages had been given insulin. Ten of them had been carried into the emergency ward in coma. All ten had revived from the coma. Forty-six patients were reported improved. Six of them were almost completely recovered. "Fred Banting is moving in the right direction at last."

And in the nick of time to preserve the lives of such men as King George V of England, Hugh Walpole, George Eastman, H. G. Wells and Dr George R. Minot. Thanks to the insulin treatment, Dr Minot was spared to the world for the discovery of an equally great gift of mercy—the liver treatment for the fatal disease of pernicious anemia.

At last Banting received his due recompense—the Nobel Prize for Medicine (1922). This prize was awarded jointly to him and to Professor Macleod. As soon as Banting received the prize money he sent half of it to his assistant, Charlie Best. In the telegram that accompanied the check he wrote: "You are with me in my share—always."

VI

AFTER THE BATTLE OF FLANDERS Fred Banting had received the iron cross for "coolness under fire." He now proved himself equally cool under a different sort of fire—a barrage of distinctions and honors. The Canadian Government organized the Banting Research Foundation to carry on his work and granted him an annuity of fifteen hundred pounds. The citizens of Toronto built an institute (1930) in his name. King George V created him (1934) a Knight Commander of the Order of the British Empire. The Royal Society named him to a Fellowship (1935) for his "outstanding contribution" to the knowledge of diabetes. "All I know about diabetes," he remarked, "can be told in about fifteen minutes." He took all his honors with a smile and went modestly on with his work.

He had now extended his work to other fields. He had entered upon a series of experiments on the suprarenal gland and on the causes of cancer. There were so many problems still unexplored. How could he rest? "It is not within the power of the properly constituted human mind to be satisfied." Once an answer comes to a question, one must search in its constituents for a new question, for the blessed realm of a new anxiety, where at the journey's end new medals may be won. Not that the medals are worth anything once they are received. "The greatest joy in life is the getting, not the having"—the consciousness of an important job well done. And what if others have taken the credit for your work? This only proves the importance of the work. "It is not the thinker that counts in human progress, but the thought." The thinker dies, but the thought lives on.

When the hours of patient searching were over, Banting took a brush and canvas and tramped over the countryside sketching the scenes before him. For painting was his means of relaxation. And he was clever at it. "Banting is one of Canada's most exciting amateur artists," remarked his colleague, Best. For many years he had apprenticed himself stubbornly to a mastery of landscape painting. It was a labor of love, this recording of his affection for the soil. He liked to paint nature in her winter as well as in her summer moods. He enjoyed tramping over the fields on his snowshoes while the winds whistled in from the gulf and Quebec was a-tingle with the cold. At noon he stopped to build a fire, thawing his hands over his tea and warming his mind with his thoughts. And then, when his fingers made contact with the paint, they were alive with power. It was such fun to escape from the stuffy little cubbyhole of his experiments to this laboratory of the outdoors. So good to breathe this peaceful air . . .

And then, a sudden halt to his peaceful experiments and his painting. The autumn of 1939. The second World War had broken out. In an old shabby suit spotted with cigarette ashes he turned up at a hospital base in Ottawa and asked for Colonel Rae, the officer in charge. "I'm too old to fight, sir, but I'd like to join up with your medical unit with the lowest ranking you can give me."

They gave him the rank of captain and he protested violently. "I would much prefer to be a private." They raised him to the rank of major and he protested still more violently. Finally, when they threatened to raise him to the rank of colonel, he consented to serve as major. "A man can try his best," he said with a resigned smile, "even in an exalted post."

VII

HE WAS FORTY-NINE. In the darkness of the world's autumn, once more a stubborn groping research to combat a malignant disease—an assault on human freedom. He aided in establishing and in classifying reserves of blood to supply transfusions for the troops and the civilians under fire. He took several trips to England as medical liaison officer. He was appointed chairman of a committee organized for the purpose of correlating the medical research work of the Canadian and the British armies.

In February 1941 he took off in a bomber for London—the stubborn capital that was keeping its good right arm flung high in a challenge when the Nazi buccaneers of the air threatened to amputate it.

There was much to be done for her—the stubborn lady London. Fred Banting was on the threshold of a new devotion, a new life of service. Now he was high above Newfoundland, headed toward the sea, busy with a special problem. Those young men of the Royal Air Force who took steep drops in dive bombers, was there not a way to keep them from losing their brief moments of consciousness as they pulled out into the higher altitudes again?

His head nodded drowsily. He looked down over the silhouetted landscape. It was the motionless face of his mother, concealed in a shroud. But he knew her beauty—he had often transferred to his canvas the shadows of her features and the sunlight in her eyes. "I shall devote much more time to painting when the war ends . . ."

The radio operator rushed over to him. "Orders from the pilot, Sir Frederick. You must bail out at once!"

An outstretched wing of the ship hit an old tree. One of the landing wheels crashed through the frozen ice of a lake. The wreckage of the plane became imbedded in five feet of snow.

The injured pilot stumbled over to the cabin. The radio operator was dead. Banting lay quiet with his eyes wide open and the blood streaming from a gash in his head. The pilot tried to rouse him. His lips moved. With a great effort of the will he began to speak—rapidly, nervously, as if he were at his desk dictating memoranda to his secretary or in the classroom delivering a lecture. The pilot produced a pencil and paper and pretended to take down the notes. But he couldn't make head or tail of them. He knew that this was the effort of a great mind to record its final message—perhaps a new formula for the stamping out of another disease. But the formula would never reach the world. . . .

Night fell and Banting passed for a few hours into a fitful sleep. With the coming of the dawn he awoke, lifted his head and continued to speak. Intermittently he fell asleep, then struggled back to consciousness and kept on dictating his incoherent notes.

The pilot realized that he must get help and get it soon, or Doctor Banting would not live through the day. Feebly he stumbled through a wilderness of rock and bush and ice. The wind blew into his face and stopped his forward progress after a pitiably short advance. His swollen legs were numb with the cold. He turned around and crawled back to the plane. Doctor Banting had somehow freed himself from the wreckage and had struggled into the open, five feet away.

This was the last of his stubborn acts. He was silent now.

EINSTEIN

Great Scientific Contributions by Einstein

Formulated the theory of relativity.

Established a mathematical basis for the structure of the universe.

Replaced the "gravitational attraction" theory of Newton with the theory of a "gravitational field in the time-space continuum."

BOOKS AND TREATISES:
Principle of Relativity.
Time, Space and Gravitation.
Ether and Relativity.
On the Method of Theoretical Physics.

Einstein

Albert Einstein

1879–

ONE day his father brought him a compass. It was a small
toy to amuse the child. Albert trembled with excitement as he
gazed upon the "magic" needle turning toward the north. He
saw before him not a plaything but a miracle. He was too
young to understand the principle of magnetism, yet instinctively
he felt that he was standing upon the threshold of an enchanted world.

It was the same way with the little fellow when he played
the violin. His eyes glistened, and his hand shook far too passionately for a healthy youngster. It was the music that so
agitated him. Very often he would stand as if in a trance while
his mother played a Mozart or a Beethoven sonata on the
piano. But when the talk turned to politics and people spoke of
Bismarck and the rise of the German Empire, Albert would grow
frightened and leave the room.

He was a queer child. Not much like the son of an electrical
engineer. One day a regiment of the Kaiser's soldiers marched
through the streets of Munich and "all the good Germans"
flocked to the windows to cheer. The children especially were
fascinated at the sight of the flashing helmets and the arrogant

goose-step of the soldiers. But Albert Einstein shuddered. He despised and feared these "fighting monsters." He begged his mother to take him away to a land where he would never have to become one of them. And his mother, to quiet her son, promised that she would.

A queer child indeed. He had none of the enthusiasms, and little of the mentality, of other children. His father was pained at the reports from Albert's teachers. They told him that the boy was mentally slow, unsociable, "adrift forever in his foolish dreams." They nicknamed him *Pater Langweil—Father Bore.* But Albert was unaware of the anxiety of his elders. He felt very keenly alive in a world full of wonder. And he probed into this world all by himself. He needed no other company. He composed songs and set them to words in praise of God. He played in his garden or walked in the streets singing his songs aloud. He was incredibly happy.

But soon he was to learn bitter things. At home he had been brought up in the Jewish faith. At the state school he was instructed in the Catholic religion. And the heart of the child found nothing irreconcilable between the Old Testament and the New. They were both beautiful poems, sad and true, these stories about the sufferings of the Prophets and the martyrdom of the Saviour. He loved both stories with an equal fervor, just as he loved his compass and his songs. But one day the teacher brought into the classroom a large nail. And he told the students that this was the nail with which Jesus had been crucified. And suddenly all eyes were turned upon Albert, as if *he* had crucified Jesus. He saw the faces of his fellow students transfixed with a strange kind of hatred. And he couldn't understand it. His face blushing with shame—for the others, not for himself—he rose from his seat and rushed out of the room.

He was alone, save for the companionship of his books. He formed a friendship across the centuries with Euclid, Newton, Spinoza, Descartes—mathematicians and philosophers whose works he had mastered before he was fifteen. And he adored the poets and the musicians—Heine, Schiller, Goethe, Beethoven, Mozart and Bach. Here was a world of order, of harmony, of law—a logic that reacted as a balm upon a sensitive nature bewildered by the illogic of his teachers and his fellow pupils.

When Albert was in the secondary school he found it more necessary than ever to "drown his solitude in his books." For his father had lost his business and had moved his family to Milan in the hope that the change of scenery might bring back his financial health. Albert was left alone in Munich.

On his vacations, however, he visited Milan and found the Italian atmosphere congenial to his dreaming soul. He renounced his German citizenship. But he didn't apply for Italian papers. He desired to remain unattached—a citizen of the world.

His father was annoyed at his eccentricities. The time had come for Albert to shoulder the responsibilities of a man. He was already sixteen. Herr Einstein urged him to forget his "philosophical nonsense" and to apply himself to the "sensible trade" of electrical engineering.

Albert was desolate. His very instincts rebelled at the idea of his becoming a tradesman. But how could he stand up against the whole world?

He got the answer to this problem one day when he read an essay of Emerson's. "If a man plant himself indomitably on his instincts, the world will come round to him."

II

ALBERT'S STUBBORNNESS won out. His father allowed him to specialize in mathematics. He took the entrance examinations for the Zurich Polytechnic Academy—and failed. He was deficient in his knowledge of foreign languages.

Back to the secondary school and his study of syntax. After a brief and intensive application to his prepositions and his participles he presented himself once more as a candidate for the Zurich Polytechnic Academy. This time he was successful.

His plans had now matured. He would prepare himself for a teaching position in mathematics and in physics. Voraciously he read every book he could find on these subjects. But his intellectual appetite had extended to several of the kindred fields in philosophy and in science. He yielded to the spell of Ernst Mach's positivism and of Darwin's evolution. He absorbed the utopian economics of socialism. He admired the methodical pessimism of Schopenhauer and the methodical optimism of Kant. And always, as in childhood, he developed his intellectual dreams within the framework of his passion for music. He visited the Music Hall and listened to the magic of Joachim's violin. And then he retired to his lodging and improvised on his own violin until late into the night.

And thus he finished his studies and received his teacher's certificate. But he received no teacher's appointment. He was a Jew. Wherever he applied for a position, he was met with the same evasive answer: "Personally I have no objection; but there are others, you see . . ."

For a while he resorted—unsuccessfully—to private tutoring, and then he got a clerical job at the Swiss patent office in Berne. Hour after hour he bent over his desk adding his figures and dreaming of the stars. In his spare moments he covered his note paper with complicated mathematical formulas. But when he heard the footsteps of his employer, he threw the paper into the waste basket. Dr Halle, kindly as he was, had no sympathy for the "speculative nonsense" of his young employee's mathematical studies.

But to Einstein these studies of his spare moments were anything but speculative. His abstract formulas had taken on the texture of reality. He had found, he believed, a new key to the riddle of the universe. But he confided this belief to only a few of his intimates—and to Mileva Maric, his Serbian schoolmate whom he had made his wife. "I have been trying to solve the problem of space and time."

When he finished what he regarded as the correct solution to the problem, he brought it into the office of the *Annalen der Physik*. "I would be happy," he said timidly to the editor, "if you could find the room to publish this in your paper."

The editor found the room, and the obscure clerk of the Swiss patent office became one of the most famous scientists in the world.

III

EINSTEIN was twenty-six when he solved the problem of celestial harmony. It was the solution of the artist as well as of the scientist. He had tried to analyze the pattern of the stars just as the musician analyzes the pattern of the sonata. How are the parts interrelated in order to produce the concordance of the whole?

All the earlier attempts to solve the structure of the universe, observed Einstein, had been based upon a false assumption. The scientists had supposed that whatever seemed true to *them,* looking out upon the universe from their *own* point of view, from their *own* relative position in their *own* little corner of the world, must necessarily be true for *everybody else,* looking out upon the universe from *every other* point of view. But actually—asserted Einstein—there is no such absolute truth. The same landscape presents different faces to different people looking upon it from different vantage points. It is one thing to the pedestrian, quite another thing to the motorist, and still another thing to the aviator. Every experience is *relative* to the person who undergoes that particular experience. The only objective reality in the universe is that which constitutes *a combination of every possible point of experience*. Absolute truth can be ascertained only through the sum total of all relative observations. This is but a mathematical way of restating the Spinozist doctrine that the Mind of God is the combination of all human minds encompassed within the framework of eternity—*sub specie aeternitatis*. Einstein was a thoroughgoing disciple of Spinoza.

But not of Newton. Contrary to the doctrine of Newton that everything tends naturally to remain at rest, Einstein declared that everything is actually in a state of motion. But the velocities of the various moving bodies of the universe, he explained, are relative to one another. To this relativity of motion, however, there is one exception—the constant velocity of light. This velocity—about 186,000 miles a second—is the maximum speed that we know. It is the one unchanging factor in all our equations about the relative speed of moving bodies.

The law of relativity, declared Einstein, applies not only to the *speed* but also to the *direction* of a moving body. Suppose we drop a stone from a tower to the ground. To us the stone will appear to fall in a straight line. To a theoretical observer in space—to Einstein an "observer" meant either a person or a recording instrument—the stone would describe a curved line, inasmuch as this observer would record not only the motion of the stone upon our planet but also the motion of our planet around its axis. To still another observer, stationed not in empty space but on another planet, subject to a different motion from that of our own planet, the falling stone would describe still another path. All the paths, or directions, of a moving object are therefore relative to the various vantage points from which the movements of the object are observed.

And so we find that both the *speed* and the *direction* of a moving body are relative. But this, continues Einstein, is not yet the whole story. There is a third factor in relativity—the relative *size* of a moving body. All bodies contract in motion. To an observer sitting inside a rapidly moving train the train is longer than it is to another observer who watches it from the outside. The rate of the contraction of a moving object increases with its increasing speed. A stick measuring a yard in a state of so-called rest would shrink to zero if it were set in motion at the speed of light.

Space, then, is relative. So, too—declares Einstein—is time. The past, the present and the future are merely three points in time analogous to the three points in space occupied by—let us say—Washington, New York and Boston. Scientifically speaking, it is just as logical to travel from tomorrow to yesterday as it is to travel from Boston to Washington. To an impartial observer of the universe all time, like all space, would be present in a single glance.

Time, like space, is a matter of relative motion. If a man could attain a speed greater than the speed of light—which of course is humanly impossible—he would overtake his past and leave the date of his birth in the future. He would see effects before their causes and he would see events before they actually occurred. Time is merely a planetary clock that measures motion. Each moving planet has its own system of local time which differs from all other time systems. The time system of the earth, far from being an absolute measurement for time everywhere, is nothing but a local schedule of the earth's rotation around the sun. A day is a measurement of motion through space. Our own point in time depends wholly upon our own position in space. The light which brings us the image of a distant star may have traveled through space for a million years before it reached the earth. Hence the star that we see today is the star of a million years ago. Similarly an event that took place upon the earth thousands of years ago—like the Battle of Marathon—may have just reached the eyes of an observer on another planet who consequently looks upon this event as an episode of today.

Today upon this planet, therefore, may be yesterday upon another planet and tomorrow upon a third planet. For time is a dimension of space—and space is a dimension of time. Actually —asserts Einstein—the universe consists of a space-time continuity; both space and time are dependent upon each other. Neither can be expressed independently. Both must be considered as coördinate aspects of motion in our mathematical approach to reality. The world is not three-dimensional. It consists of the three dimensions of space and of an additional fourth dimension—time.

IV

EINSTEIN was amused at the flurry of attention that he received for his "superior" wisdom. "Before God we are all equally wise, equally foolish," he said. He wasn't the least bit excited when he received the offer of a professorship at Zurich. Professors had always bored him. He was an artist. He had no use for the pedantic type of mind. "Pedants collect their facts as dogs collect their bones—only to hoard them in the dust." Few of the so-called scholars, he had noticed, understood the meaning of speculative thought. Hardly any of them were dreamers. They laughed when you told them that it is possible for the scientist to search for the secret of physical laws just as passionately as the composer searches for the secret of musical harmony. "The great scientist and the great composer are alike in one respect—both of them are great poets."

It was as a poet that Einstein greeted the arrival of his first child. He took far greater joy in wheeling the baby carriage than in delivering his lectures at the university. He trembled before the vacuous eyes and the gaping mouths of the audiences who had come to purchase a penny's worth of knowledge at the fountain of his wisdom. He was not a man to lead crowds or to teach crowds or to mingle in crowds. He was a solitary student, "a singular, taciturn, lonely seeker." It mattered little to him that he had built up a solid reputation amongst the learned societies of Europe, that the distinguished mathematician, Poincaré, had greeted him as the "conqueror of Newton" and that the eminent physicist, Lorentz, had acknowledged him as one of the foremost scientists of history. It was unessential that the famous universities of Utrecht and of Leyden had offered him professorships. He looked back regretfully upon the old days when he had served as a clerk under Dr Halle—a position in which he had found the time and the quiet to carry on his researches without ceremony, without ostentation, without banquets.

He finally accepted the position of *professor ordinarius* at the University of Berlin. For his family must live somehow. During his walks through the streets of the Prussian capital he continued to build upon his theory of relativity. His early speculations had led to a great number of interesting conclusions. But they had given rise to an equally great number of further questions. A "demoniacal curiosity" had taken possession of him to seek out the final lair of truth—the underlying cadence in the movement of the stars through the symphony of time and space. More and more in his moments of relaxation he turned to his violin and improvised new themes that gave wing to his speculative thoughts.

But there was a sudden interruption to these thoughts. Europe had exploded into war (1914). The sensitive soul of Einstein recoiled in dismay. "This war is a vicious and savage crime. I would rather be hacked to pieces than take part in such an abominable business."

But few people now listened to him. Creative thought had no place in a world bent upon destruction. It was all a matter of relative values . . .

Throughout the conflict Einstein lived in a cosmos of his own creation. Shutting himself up in a shabby little attic away from the other rooms in a Berlin apartment house, he set to work verifying and elaborating upon the essential principles of his theory of relativity. The slightest domestic episode was enough to start him off on a significant train of thought. Once he climbed a ladder to change a picture on the wall. But absent-mindedly he forgot the business at hand, lost his footing and landed on the floor. When he got to his feet he commenced to speculate on the causes of the upset. The fall of the ladder in Einstein's attic was destined to play no less important a role in science than the fall of the apple in Newton's garden. For it led Einstein to undertake a critical analysis of the theory of gravitation.

Once more, as in the analysis of motion and space and time, he arrived at startling conclusions. The physicists, he declared, had been fundamentally wrong in their belief that objects *fell*, in the sense that they were *pulled down* to a center of gravitation. Scientifically speaking, no object is ever pulled down. Indeed, there is no such thing as "down"—or "up"—in the universe. "The motion of a body is due solely to the tendency of matter to follow the path of least resistance." Bodies in their travels through space select the easiest paths and avoid the most difficult. There is no more reason to assume an absolute gravitational force through space than to assume an absolute dimension of time. Just as there are local schedules of time, so too there are local fields of gravitation. But these fields have no mysterious force or pull. Every mass—like the sun, for example—creates at its center a curving or "warping" of the neighboring space into a "hill." And the masses in the vicinity of that hill—like the earth and the other planets of the solar system—move around the slopes of that hill for the simple reason that this is the easiest way for them to move. Einstein proved this "curvature" theory of space by means of a series of mathematical formulas. The significant point of the theory is this: The shortest distance between two points is not a *straight* line, but a *curved* line, since the universe consists of a series of curved hills and all objects in this universe travel around the curved slopes of these hills. Indeed, in this universe of ours there is no such thing as motion in a straight line. A ray of light traveling toward the earth from a distant star is deflected, or turned aside, when it passes the hill-slope of space around the sun. Einstein figured out mathematically the exact degree of this deflection.

And his figure proved to be correct. At the eclipse of 1919 the observatories of Cambridge and of Greenwich, each acting independently of the other, sent out an expedition of astronomers to photograph the direction of the starlight during the eclipse. Both groups found that their photographs corroborated the prediction of Einstein almost to the exact decimal point which he had figured out in his mathematical formulas. The ray of light *did* curve in the manner and the degree as described in the calculations of Einstein. A new conception of the universe had been born in the human mind.

When Einstein received the photographs of the astronomers he looked at them with a cynical twinkle in his eye. "Now that my theory of relativity has been proved true," he chuckled, "Germany will claim me as a German and France will declare that I am a citizen of the world. Had my theory proved false, France would have said that I am a German and Germany would have declared that I am a Jew."

V

No ONE was more surprised at the sudden deluge of fame that descended upon Einstein than the scientist himself. Like Byron he awoke one day to find his name on everybody's lips. Not only learned men of science but millions of common people throughout the world had adopted him as a household idol. The results of the astronomers' expedition had been telegraphed to all the newspapers. He was kept busy posing for photographs, submitting to interviews, turning down offers from Hollywood— including one invitation to make a film at forty thousand dollars a week. In his bewilderment he turned to his wife. "This won't last. It *can't* last. People have gone temporarily crazy and tomorrow they will forget all about it." Fame was the last thing he desired. As his notoriety kept increasing from month to month he became frankly annoyed. He had hoped to spend his entire life in quiet research. And now he couldn't hear his own thoughts for the noisy acclamation. What did people want with him? Why would they not permit him to live like anyone else? What barbarous nonsense was all this? "Everybody talks about me, and nobody understands me."

Indeed, nobody even *cared* to understand this amazing

juggler of mathematical ideas. One evening a young lady introduced her fiancé to the pastor of her church. The following day the pastor met the bride-to-be and took her aside. "I approve of your young man in every respect save one," he told her. "He lacks a sense of humor. I asked him to explain to me Einstein's theory of relativity and he actually tried to do it."

Einstein's popularity had risen to appalling heights. He couldn't take his daily walk in the streets without being surrounded by photographers, reporters and autograph hunters. Every day baskets of mail arrived at the little Berlin apartment. Famous statesmen, obscure pacifists, unemployed workmen, lovelorn ladies—everybody wrote to him. The supreme irony had settled upon him. "I have become a demigod in spite of myself." A young devotee volunteered to be his disciple in "cosmic meditation." An inventor confided to him his plans for a new flying machine. A would-be explorer asked his advice on a trip to the Asiatic jungles. An actor begged him to become his manager. A cigar manufacturer announced that he had produced a new brand of cigars and named it *Relativity*.

"The public looks upon me as a strange new animal in the circus of the world." He smiled. And he tried to go on with his work in his quiet, modest way. When he was invited to speak to a distinguished group of scientists at Oslo, he pulled out a shabby dinner jacket and brushed it carefully. "If anyone thinks I am not dressed elegantly enough," he told his wife, "I'll put a tag on this coat with the notice that it has just been brushed." He arrived for another of his lectures—at the University of Berlin —in a homely pair of sport knickers and sandals. He walked about the streets of Berlin wrapped in an old sweater and in new dreams. Let the circus-minded public gossip and glare. He would be just simply himself.

His simplicity was no theatrical pose on his part. Once the queen of Belgium invited him to pay her a visit. Never suspecting that a reception committee of state dignitaries would await him at the station in their limousine, he alighted from the train with a suitcase in one hand and a violin in the other and started on foot for the palace.

In vain the dignitaries looked for him at the station. Finally they returned to the queen with the announcement that Einstein had apparently changed his mind about coming. And then they espied the dusty figure of a little gray-haired man tramping up the road.

"Why didn't you use the car I sent for you, Herr Doktor?" asked the queen.

Her guest looked at her with a naïve smile. "It was a very pleasant walk, Your Majesty."

He asked for no limousines in his journey through life. All he wanted was just "a very pleasant walk." He was disturbed when the crowds lined the way and cluttered up the landscape of his thoughts. They made such unreasonable demands upon him. When the editor of a successful American magazine offered him a staggering fee for an article on any subject that he might care to discuss, tears of rage sprang into his eyes. "Does the impudent fellow think I am a movie star?" he cried to his wife.

He hated wealth. He would have none of it. "I am absolutely convinced that no wealth in the world can help humanity forward." What the world wanted most, he said, could never be bought with money. "The world has been ravaged by war. The old hatreds are festering. The world needs permanent peace and lasting good will."

When the war was over, he tried to establish his dream of world peace upon a basis of reality. He undertook a series of "reconciliation lectures" in the "enemy" countries. At a time when it was dangerous to speak German in the streets of Paris the scientist in a gentle voice explained his cosmic philosophy and won the entire audience back to a sympathy for his German countrymen. When he stood on a London platform the quiet hostility with which the audience first greeted him as a German melted into tolerance and swelled finally to loud acclaim. The universality of his thinking made people ashamed of their puny provincialism. He showed them the design of an interstellar harmony. And he foretold that some day there would be a similar harmonious design among the nations on the earth.

He met Aristide Briand, the French premier, and discussed with him the necessity of a Franco-German pact to end hatred. He accepted a post as the German representative of the League of Nations committee for intellectual coöperation, and he discussed with Henri Bergson the architecture of the "New Republic of Decency" that the men of good will were bent upon raising throughout the world. "It is plain that we exist for our fellow men—in the first place for those upon whose smiles and welfare all our happiness depends, and next for all those unknown to us personally but to whose destinies we are bound by the tie of sympathy."

Others were not so convinced of his credo. He barely escaped assassination at the hands of a Russian noblewoman who harbored imperialistic ambitions. All over the world the gentle scientist who had desired nothing more than an opportunity for his private studies—unless it be public justice for his fellow men—became a target for political abuse. Cries were raised against him on the grounds of his racial origin. Antisemitism had caught post-war Germany in full tide. He was aghast at the savage intolerance of his German countrymen, but he felt convinced that under the right kind of leadership they might yet return to the sanity of their old time cultural and moral standards. When he found his name high on the black list of the German right-wing assassins he crossed over to the refuge of Holland.

But he encountered the ferment of unrest even in that tolerant country. Indeed everywhere in the world humanity seemed to be beating a hasty retreat to barbarism. People had lost their sense of proportion. The Mark Twain Society offered him the position of honorary vice-president. But when he learned that this society had offered a similar post to Benito Mussolini, Einstein flatly rejected the dishonor.

He went on a journey to the Orient. In India he was shocked

to see millions of men living in slave labor and transporting their fellow men literally upon their backs. He refused to become a party to such human degradation. He never rode in a rickshaw throughout his entire trip. He went to China and saw men and women and children groaning aloud at their work in the cotton mills. He visited Japan and discounted the ceremonious treatment he received at the hands of the grownups. Instead, he turned to the Japanese children. He accepted from them scrapbooks of their drawings. And he listened with joy to their talk. "In the children lies the hope of the world." They must never be brought up to hate. They must never abuse the hard-won achievements of the human race. "Let us hope," he told his little friends, "that your generation will put mine to shame."

VI

THE wandering philosopher-minstrel, with his mathematical formulas and his violin, traveled on to Palestine and Spain and Latin America. Finally he arrived in the United States. And here at last he found a land where human beings of all classes lived together in tolerable friendship.

One day in November 1932, while Einstein was talking to a group of scientists on the Pacific Coast, a winter storm broke with fury in Berlin. Adolf Hitler took over the affairs of the German people.

The German Government, hoping to receive the indorsement of the "world-builder" for the Nazi regime, begged Einstein to return. Hitler would "overlook the fact that he was a Jew." But Einstein refused. And so Hitler put a price of twenty thousand marks upon his head. A band of storm troopers broke into his summer home at Caputh on the charge that he had concealed a quantity of arms and ammunition with which to overturn the government. They found in the "arsenal" nothing that resembled "arms" except an old bread knife grown rusty with disuse.

Hounded from his native land—the Nazis had received his resignation from the University of Berlin "without regret"—he accepted a professorship at Princeton. Here he hoped to go on, peacefully and quietly, with his old academic curriculum of human friendships and cosmic dreams.

At the present writing he mingles with the professors and the students and the townsfolk and the Greek who keeps the restaurant and the Italian who runs the barber shop on Nassau Street. He has received his citizenship papers. "I am an American now!" he remarked proudly on the day of his naturalization. He is placid and even optimistic beneath a shock of hair that has long turned white and eyes that have suffered and a forehead whose deep wrinkles make him look older than his years.

Often now he sits in the darkness of his study and smokes his pipe—too assiduously, his doctor warns him, for his heart is weak and the smoking does it no good. And Elsa, his (second) wife who always was so careful to limit him to the doctor's prescribed budget, has passed along. The smoke from his pipe whirls into complicated spirals that defy even the mind of a mathematician. A strange, inexplicable mystery—this universe with its spirals of smoke and its whirlpools of nebulae and its generations of hating, fighting men. Will it ever be given to any scientist to arrive at the final solution? And always when he considers this question he finds comfort in a single word—*Courage!*